CAMBRIDGE MONOGRAPHS ON PHYSICS

GENERAL EDITORS

N. FEATHER, F.R.S.
Professor of Natural Philosophy in the University of Edinburgh

D. SHOENBERG, PH.D.
Fellow of Gonville and Caius College, Cambridge

THERMAL DIFFUSION IN GASES

THERMAL DIFFUSION
IN GASES

BY

K. E. GREW
University College, Exeter

AND

T. L. IBBS
University of Birmingham

CAMBRIDGE
AT THE UNIVERSITY PRESS

1952

PUBLISHED BY
THE SYNDICS OF THE CAMBRIDGE UNIVERSITY PRESS

London Office: Bentley House, N.W. 1
American Branch: New York

Agents for Canada, India, and Pakistan: Macmillan

Printed in Great Britain at the University Press, Cambridge
(Brooke Crutchley, University Printer)

GENERAL PREFACE

The Cambridge Physical Tracts, out of which this series of Monographs has developed, were planned and originally published in a period when book production was a fairly rapid process. Unfortunately, that is no longer so, and to meet the new situation a change of title and a slight change of emphasis have been decided on. The major aim of the series will still be the presentation of the results of recent research, but individual volumes will be somewhat more substantial, and more comprehensive in scope, than were the volumes of the older series. This will be true, in many cases, of new editions of the Tracts, as these are republished in the expanded series, and it will be true in most cases of the Monographs which have been written since the War or are still to be written.

The aim will be that the series as a whole shall remain representative of the entire field of pure physics, but it will occasion no surprise if, during the next few years, the subject of nuclear physics claims a large share of attention. Only in this way can justice be done to the enormous advances in this field of research over the War years.

N. F.
D. S.

AUTHORS' PREFACE

This monograph deals with thermal diffusion in gases, with the application of thermal diffusion to the separation of gas mixtures, and with the related phenomenon called the diffusion thermoeffect; it includes also a brief account of thermal diffusion in liquids. Its chief concern is with the experimental work, the volume of which is now considerable. What theory there is is based closely on that given by Chapman in his many papers and in *The Mathematical Theory of Non-Uniform Gases* by Chapman and Cowling. Reference to this work is necessary for more theoretical information than can be given here, particularly about the equations of diffusion and thermal flux which are effectively our starting points. To facilitate this, we have adopted the notation used by Chapman and Cowling; the only point requiring mention for a reading of this monograph is the use of $\partial/\partial \mathbf{r}$ to represent the operator usually denoted by '∇'.

We have not attempted to discuss the recent developments in the thermodynamical treatment of thermal diffusion. These are described in two monographs dealing with irreversible processes in general—*Thermodynamics of Irreversible Processes* by S. R. de Groot (Amsterdam, 1951), and *Thermodynamics of the Steady State* by K. G. Denbigh (Methuen, 1951).

We are much indebted to Professor Sydney Chapman, who has for many years been a source of help and stimulus. But for his theoretical foundation and physical insight our experiments would not have been started; and it is unlikely that, without his encouragement, they would have been continued. To Professor T. G. Cowling we are grateful for comment and criticism while the manuscript was being prepared, for suggestions about the theoretical treatment of the diffusion thermoeffect, and especially for the account of the method of solution of the Boltzmann equation which is given here. We thank also Dr R. Fürth and Dr H. London for reading and commenting upon parts of the manuscript, and those who have given us permission to reproduce material from their publications.

K. E. G.
T. L. I.

CONTENTS

CHAPTER V

Comparison of Experimental and Theoretical Results

CHAPTER VI

The Diffusion Thermoeffect

CHAPTER VII

Application of Thermal Diffusion to the Separation of Gas Mixtures

CHAPTER VIII

Thermal Diffusion in Liquids: The Soret Effect

INTRODUCTION

Diffusion is said to occur in a mixture when there is a relative motion of its components. Such relative motion commonly arises because of inhomogeneity of composition. For example, in a binary mixture in which the composition is not uniform the components move in opposite directions, each down its concentration gradient, with the result that, if the temperature is uniform, the inequalities of composition are reduced and ultimately removed. Diffusion originating in this way is 'ordinary' or 'concentration' diffusion. Diffusion may, however, have other causes; in particular, it may be due to non-uniformity of temperature within a mixture. Diffusion from this cause is called thermal diffusion.

Thermal diffusion consists then in a relative motion of the components of a mixture arising from temperature differences within the mixture. It leads, therefore, in a mixture initially of uniform composition, to the development of a concentration gradient. Since this concentration gradient in turn causes ordinary diffusion tending to eliminate the gradient, a steady state is possible in which the separating effect of thermal diffusion is balanced by the remixing effect of ordinary diffusion. Whether or not such a steady state exists, it is generally true that when the temperature of a mixture is not uniform its composition also is not uniform—a temperature gradient implies a concentration gradient. We may imagine, for example, a gas mixture contained within two bulbs, one above the other, connected by a tube. If both bulbs are at the same temperature the composition of the gas is uniform. But if the temperature of the upper bulb is raised above that of the lower, the more massive molecules diffuse (usually) down the temperature gradient, the lighter molecules up the gradient, until a steady difference in composition of the mixture in the two bulbs is established. Thermal diffusion thus brings about a partial separation of the components of the initially uniform mixture.

The existence of thermal diffusion was first discovered experimentally, in liquids. In 1856 Ludwig stated that he had found differences in concentration in samples of sodium sulphate solutions taken from different parts of a vessel which was unequally heated.

This effect was investigated more fully by Soret some twenty years later. Soret (1879–81) filled a straight vertical tube with various salt solutions and set up a temperature gradient in it by heating the upper part and cooling the lower. After the lapse of about fifty days he analysed samples taken from the upper and lower parts and found that the solute was more concentrated in the lower, cooler, region than in the other. Some attempts at a theoretical explanation of this phenomenon were made, but without success.

In contrast, thermal diffusion in gases was predicted theoretically before it was observed experimentally. In the years 1911–17 the general kinetic theory of gases was developed by Enskog (1911, 1912, 1917) and independently by Chapman (1912, 1916 a, b, 1917a). The theory contains the result, unexpected at that time, that diffusion in a gas mixture may arise from the existence of a temperature gradient as well as a concentration gradient. Experimental confirmation of this result came first from an experiment made by Chapman and Dootson (1917). Chapman and Dootson filled two bulbs connected together by a tube with a mixture of hydrogen and carbon dioxide or hydrogen and sulphur dioxide. One bulb was then heated to about 200° C. for some hours, after which the gas in the two bulbs was analysed. It was found that for mixtures in which the components were in roughly equal proportions, the hydrogen content of the mixture in the hot bulb was greater, by 2 or 3 %, than that of the gas in the cold bulb.

Although the experimental demonstration of thermal diffusion in gases is relatively recent, an effect which may be regarded as the converse of thermal diffusion had been known much earlier. Dufour in 1873 had shown that the diffusion of one gas into another initially at the same temperature results in the establishment of a transient temperature gradient. This 'diffusion thermoeffect' has been investigated again in recent years, particularly by Waldmann (1943–9). The possibility of such an effect appears, of course, in the Chapman-Enskog theory.

A considerable stimulus was given to the study of thermal diffusion and the related phenomena when Clusius and Dickel (1938) showed how thermal diffusion could be utilized to separate almost completely the components of a gas mixture. In studying the thermal diffusion effect experimentally the usual procedure is to measure the concentration gradient which results when a temperature gradient is established in a mixture. It is clearly necessary to avoid disturbance due to convection currents, and with this aim the gradient has usually been arranged vertically. Clusius and Dickel, however, used a horizontal gradient, the mixture being contained within a vertical glass tube along the axis of which was a nichrome wire which could be heated electrically. The temperature gradient thus established in the mixture produces two effects: first, a partial separation of the components due to a transverse thermal diffusion; secondly, a convective flow of the gas up the hotter surface and down the cooler. As a result of this convection, any one element of the mixture is continually juxtaposed with another with which it is not in equilibrium as regards its composition. Its composition, therefore, changes continuously as it moves up or down within the tube. The change thus effected in the composition of the gas in the reservoirs is many times greater than that which is produced by thermal diffusion alone. Clusius and Dickel succeeded by this means in separating almost completely first the isotopes of chlorine, and subsequently those of several other elements.

The importance of thermal diffusion is thus both practical and theoretical. The magnitude of the effect, in gases at least, is strongly dependent on the nature of the forces exerted by one molecule on another, and the study of thermal diffusion is one of the best means of investigating these forces. It is this aspect of thermal diffusion which is treated most fully in what follows. Chapters I–V consist of an introduction to the theory of thermal diffusion in gases, an account of experimental methods and results, and the correlation of the results with the theory. In Chapter VI the related phenomenon, the diffusion thermoeffect, is discussed. Chapter VII describes the application of thermal diffusion to the separation of the components of gas mixtures. Chapter VIII contains a short account of thermal diffusion in the liquid phase; this is brief because there already exists a monograph on this subject—*L'Effet Soret*, by S. R. de Groot (1945)—and because the theory is less developed than that for gases.

CHAPTER I

DISCOVERY AND NATURE OF THE EFFECT

1.1. Discovery of the effect

The possibility of thermal diffusion was discovered in the course of the extension of the kinetic theory to the case of gases which are in non-equilibrium states, and in which therefore the velocity distribution is different from the familiar Maxwellian distribution, which applies only to the state of equilibrium. The more general theory is necessary for the exact treatment of viscosity, conduction and diffusion because a gas in which one or more of these phenomena appear is clearly not in a state of equilibrium.

The first attempt to deal with a gas in a non-equilibrium state was made by Maxwell (1867, 1879). Maxwell's work, however, is restricted to a particular molecular model. It happens that the mathematical difficulties, otherwise formidable, are much reduced if it is assumed that the molecules can be regarded as centres of repulsive force varying inversely as the fifth power of the distance. It was for this model—now referred to as the Maxwellian molecule—that Maxwell developed his theory. The possibility of thermal diffusion does not appear in it because, as will be seen later, it is just for this type of molecular interaction that the thermal diffusion coefficient vanishes. It was Enskog and Chapman who, independently and almost simultaneously, established the theory in the general case. In 1911 Enskog gave the theory for a gas mixture of a special type—a Lorentzian gas (§2.5)—and pointed out that the theory led to the conclusion that diffusion in a gas mixture could be caused by a temperature gradient as well as by a concentration gradient. In a later paper (1917) he extended the theory to the general case and gave expressions for the transport coefficients including thermal diffusion. Meanwhile, Chapman (1912, 1916a, b, 1917a) had attacked the problem by a different method. He gave the general kinetic theory first of a simple then of a composite gas and discovered again the phenomenon of thermal diffusion. It is of interest to note that his general equation of diffusion contains a term representing diffusion due to a pressure gradient as well as the term involving the temperature gradient. Pressure diffusion, however, has been little studied because of the obvious experimental difficulties.

The work of Chapman and Enskog has been extended to take account of quantum principles by Hellund and Uehling (1939). The modifications required by quantum theory are of importance only for gases consisting of the lightest molecules at extremely low temperatures. The results given in what follows are based on classical mechanics. Hellund (1940) has also developed the theory of mixtures containing more than two components, taking into account quantum corrections. The classical theory of such mixtures has been given by Curtiss and Hirschfelder (1949). Little if any experimental work has been done on multicomponent mixtures, however, and we consider here only binary mixtures.

1.2. The equation of diffusion

The result of the general theory of Chapman and Enskog that is fundamental for our present purpose is embodied in the equation of diffusion.

Consider first a simple gas, that is, one consisting of one species of molecule only. Let the velocity of a molecule with respect to some arbitrary reference frame be denoted by $\mathbf{c}$. For a gas consisting of N molecules the mean velocity is $\bar{\mathbf{c}} = \Sigma \mathbf{c}/N$. If $\bar{\mathbf{c}}$ is zero the gas is at rest with respect to the chosen frame; otherwise the gas is moving as a whole with velocity $\bar{\mathbf{c}}$. The thermal or peculiar velocity $\mathbf{C}$ of a molecule is the difference between the velocity referred to a given frame and the mean velocity referred to the same frame; thus $\mathbf{C} = \mathbf{c} - \bar{\mathbf{c}}$, and the mean thermal velocity is clearly zero. For a mixture of two gases a mean velocity can be defined for each species of molecule. If these mean velocities are unequal, the two species are diffusing relatively to each other with velocity

$$\bar{\mathbf{c}}_1 - \bar{\mathbf{c}}_2 = \Sigma \mathbf{c}_1/N_1 - \Sigma \mathbf{c}_2/N_2,$$

where the subscripts refer to the two species 1 and 2. To find the mean velocity it is necessary to know the velocity-distribution function, that is, the function which gives the number of molecules in each small range of velocity. It is of the determination of this function for a gas mixture in a non-equilibrium state that the achievement of Chapman and Enskog essentially consists. We defer for the present any discussion of their work and merely state the fundamental equation of diffusion to which it leads. This is, for a binary mixture, subject to no external forces and in which the pressure, but not the temperature, is uniform,

$$\bar{c}_1 - \bar{c}_2 = \bar{C}_1 - \bar{C}_2 = - \frac{1}{n_{10}n_{20}} \left[D_{12}\frac{\partial n_{10}}{\partial \mathbf{r}} + D_T \frac{1}{T}\frac{\partial T}{\partial \mathbf{r}} \right], \quad (1.1)$$

where $\bar{c}_1, \bar{c}_2 =$ mean velocities of the two species of molecule; species (1) refers to the heavier molecules.

$\bar{C}_1, \bar{C}_2 =$ mean thermal velocities;

$n_{10}, n_{20} =$ volume fractions or concentrations of the two species (if n_1, n_2 are the number densities, and $n = n_1 + n_2$, then $n_{10} = n_1/n$, $n_{20} = n_2/n$);

$D_{12} =$ coefficient of ordinary (concentration) diffusion;

$D_T =$ coefficient of thermal diffusion;

$\partial\psi/\partial\mathbf{r}$ (where ψ is a scalar, e.g. n_{10} and T) $=$ grad ψ.

Both coefficients, D_T and D_{12}, are complicated functions of the relative masses and numbers of the two kinds of molecule and of quantities which depend on the nature of the forces between the molecules. We are concerned with D_T only as it appears in the ratio D_T/D_{12}; this is called the thermal diffusion ratio and is denoted by k_T. In terms of this ratio the equation of diffusion may be written

$$\bar{c}_1 - \bar{c}_2 = \bar{C}_1 - \bar{C}_2 = - \frac{D_{12}}{n_{10}n_{20}} \left[\frac{\partial n_{10}}{\partial \mathbf{r}} + k_T \frac{1}{T}\frac{\partial T}{\partial \mathbf{r}} \right]. \quad (1.2)$$

In this equation the first term in the bracket relates to diffusion due to a concentration gradient. The presence of the second term, unsuspected prior to the work of Chapman and Enskog, shows that diffusion may be caused by a temperature gradient.

The steady state. It follows from this equation that the steady state of a gas mixture, in which $\bar{C}_1 - \bar{C}_2 = 0$, implies the absence of a concentration gradient or uniformity of composition only when the temperature is uniform; if a temperature gradient exists there is also a concentration gradient such that

$$\frac{\partial n_{10}}{\partial \mathbf{r}} = - k_T \frac{1}{T}\frac{\partial T}{\partial \mathbf{r}}.$$

If this equation is integrated, assuming that k_T may be treated as a constant, we obtain

$$n_{10} - n'_{10} = k_T \ln T'/T, \qquad (1.3)$$

where n_{10} is the concentration where the temperature is T, and n'_{10} the concentration where the temperature is T'. This then is the difference in composition which should be observed when a gas mixture is confined in two interconnected bulbs at different temperatures T and T'. That such a difference in composition did exist was shown first by Chapman and Dootson in the experiment which has already been described.

The quantity $(n_{10} - n'_{10})$ is termed the separation. From measured values of the separation the thermal diffusion ratio k_T can be calculated, and by comparing these values with theoretical ones for specific molecular models, information can be derived about the nature of molecular interactions.

The theoretical expressions for the thermal diffusion ratio will be discussed later (§2.6). At this point it suffices to say that k_T, and therefore the separation, depends in a complex manner on the following factors:

(i) The ratio of the masses and of the diameters of the two species of molecule; the magnitude of k_T increases with these ratios.

(ii) The nature of the forces between the molecules, chiefly the forces between unlike molecules $(1, 2)$ but also the forces between like molecules $(1, 1)$ and $(2, 2)$. The more nearly do these interactions approach those of rigid elastic spheres the greater is the value of k_T.

(iii) The relative proportions, n_{10} and n_{20}, of the two components. The expression for k_T includes as one factor the product $n_{10} n_{20}$, so that k_T becomes vanishingly small as either component becomes rare. This strong dependence of k_T on the composition makes it useful to introduce the related quantity, the thermal diffusion factor α, defined by

$$\alpha = k_T/n_{10} n_{20}.$$

It is desirable, before going further into the theory, to illustrate these theoretical points by referring to some typical experimental results.

1.3. Early experiments

After the existence of thermal diffusion had been confirmed by Chapman and Dootson in experiments already briefly described, an extensive study of thermal diffusion was begun by Ibbs in 1919. In his first experiments Ibbs (1921) used the apparatus shown in fig. 1 which was devised by G. A. Shakespear. It consisted of a cylindrical glass vessel along the axis of which was a platinum spiral which could be heated electrically. A uniform gas mixture was passed in at A. As it moved slowly upwards the transverse temperature gradient set up between the spiral B and the cool walls caused thermal diffusion; consequently the gas drawn through C from the cooler and outer parts of the vessel was enriched in one component, and that drawn through D in the other component. Ibbs measured the difference in composition of the two streams of gas, using hydrogen-carbon dioxide mixtures of various proportions and various temperatures of the spiral. For the analysis of the mixtures the katharometer was used —an instrument which depends on the variation of the thermal conductivity of the mixture with its composition. These experiments sufficed to establish the fact that the heavier component diffuses down the temperature gradient and that the separation depends on the composition of the mixture and on the temperature roughly in accordance with the theory; the indefiniteness of the hot and cold regions from which the two streams of gas were taken precluded, however, an exact comparison.

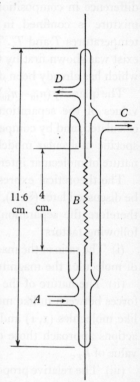

11·6 cm.   4 cm.

Fig. 1. Separation of a streaming gas mixture. A, inlet; B, heated platinum spiral; C, D, outlets. After Ibbs (1921).

In his next experiment Ibbs (1925) confined the gas mixture within two interconnected vessels which could be brought to definite temperatures, as in Chapman and Dootson's experiment, but to reduce the time required for equilibrium to be reached, the volume occupied by the gas was much reduced. The change in composition was again measured with the katharometer, and the katharometer cell itself formed one part of the diffusion vessel. Its volume was only $1 \cdot 5$ cm.^{3}. The other part was a bulb of volume $12 \cdot 1$ cm.^{3}. The katharometer cell was kept at about $10°$ C.; the temperature of the bulb was varied from 10 to $300°$ C. The apparatus is shown in fig. 2; a description of the katharometer is given below (§3.3). With this arrangement most of the change in composition occurs in the smaller volume, and as the quantity of gas to be transferred is small, the time to attain equilibrium is short— a few minutes. The separation was found as the sum of the measured change in composition in the katharometer cell and the change in the bulb calculated from this and the relative volumes and temperatures (§3.2).

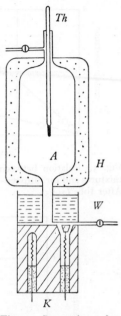

Fig. 2. Separation of a stationary gas mixture. A, glass vessel; H, heating jacket; K, katharometer; Th, thermometer; W, water bath. After Ibbs (1925).

Of the results obtained by Ibbs in this way we may take those for hydrogen-nitrogen mixtures as typical. Fig. 3 shows the variation of the separation with the relative proportions of the components, the temperatures of the bulb and cell being the same for all mixtures. In accordance with the theory the separation is a maximum when the proportions of the components are about equal. The effect of a change in the ratio of the molecular masses is seen in a comparison of the results for hydrogen-nitrogen mixtures with those, also shown in fig. 3, for nitrogen-carbon dioxide mixtures, the temperatures T, T' being the same in both cases. Fig. 4 shows how, for hydrogen-nitrogen mixtures of a given composition, the separation increases nearly proportionately with $\ln(T'/T)$, T' being the temperature of the bulb, T that of the katharometer cell. In this range of temperature the thermal diffusion ratio k_T is therefore nearly independent of temperature. Subsequently, similar experiments were made with the bulb of the diffusion apparatus at low temperatures. For this purpose the apparatus was inverted to eliminate convection

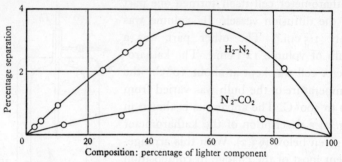

Fig. 3. Relation between separation and composition for hydrogen-nitrogen mixtures and for nitrogen-carbon dioxide mixtures; $\log (T'/T) = 0.2$ throughout. After Ibbs (1925).

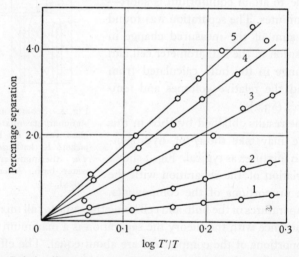

Fig. 4. Relation between separation and $\log (T'/T)$ for hydrogen-nitrogen mixtures of various compositions. Percentage hydrogen: (1) 4.7, (2) 10.7, (3) 25.7, (4) 37.4, (5) 50.5. After Ibbs (1925).

and to allow the immersion of the bulb in a refrigerant—liquid oxygen or cooled pentane. At the lowest temperatures of the bulb the separation was found to be appreciably less than that expected if the approximate proportionality with $\ln (T'/T)$ observed at higher temperatures was maintained. A curve for a hydrogen-nitrogen mixture is shown in fig. 5. These results show that the thermal diffusion ratio k_T decreases as the temperature decreases. A similar effect has been observed in all mixtures examined. The magnitude of the change in k_T over the same range in temperature T' varies appreciably from mixture to mixture, however; for those mixtures

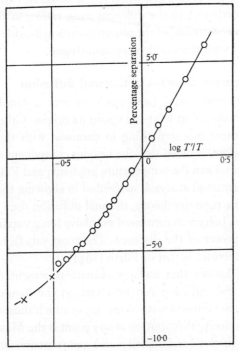

Fig. 5. Relation between separation and log (T'/T) for a hydrogen-nitrogen mixture containing 39·8 % hydrogen. $T = 293°$ K, $T' = 12 \rightarrow 600$ K. ×, van Itterbeek *et al.* (1947); ○, Grew (1949).

comprising gases with low liquefying points, such as helium-neon, the change is small.

It will be seen later that the value of the thermal diffusion ratio for a mixture of molecules of given mass and size, in given proportions, can be calculated readily when the molecules are assumed to interact as rigid elastic spheres. For this type of interaction k_T has its maximum value. It is natural therefore to use as an indication of the nature of the actual interactions in a gas mixture the ratio of the value of k_T determined experimentally to the theoretical value for the same mixture calculated on the assumption that the molecules interact as rigid spheres. This ratio, $k_T(\text{exp.})/k_T(\infty)$, has been termed the thermal separation ratio R_T. For the hydrogen-nitrogen mixtures considered above, its value at ordinary temperatures is about 0·6, for the nitrogen-carbon dioxide mixtures about 0·3. The difference in the separation observed with these two mixtures is thus only partly due to the different mass ratios; in part it is due to the relative 'softness' of the nitrogen-carbon dioxide interactions as compared with those in hydrogen-nitrogen.

1.4. Elementary theories of thermal diffusion

Several attempts have been made to give a simple theory of thermal diffusion or at least to explain its origin. Gillespie (1939), whose argument has something in common with that of Fürth, described below, showed that the heavier component of a mixture should diffuse down the temperature gradient; and Frankel (1940), using a dimensional analysis, succeeded in showing that, in agreement with the rigorous theory, thermal diffusion does not occur if the molecules behave as centres of repulsive force varying inversely as the fifth power of the distance. The most satisfactory of these elementary theories is that of Fürth (1942).

It is well known that an approximate treatment of viscosity, conduction and diffusion can be given on the assumption that, despite the non-uniform state of the gas in which these phenomena appear, the velocity distribution at any point is the Maxwellian one appropriate to the local density and temperature, and that the characteristics of the distribution at the point where a molecule makes a collision are carried by it to the point of its next collision. The transport coefficients can then be found from the expressions deduced on this basis for the flux of momentum, energy and number across a plane in the gas. Fürth has extended this treatment to include thermal diffusion somewhat as follows.

Consider a binary mixture in which both the temperature and the composition vary in the z direction. Across the plane $z = 0$ there is a net flow of molecules of the first kind (1) and an opposite flow of molecules (2). If the pressure is uniform and steady throughout the gas, as we assume, these fluxes must be equal in magnitude. The flux of either species may be regarded as consisting of two parts, the first a result of the thermal motions of the molecules, the second a result of the mass motion of the gas which is necessary to maintain uniformity of pressure. The first part is evaluated as follows.

In a gas in which the velocity distribution is Maxwellian, the number of molecules impinging on unit area moving with the mean velocity of the gas is $\frac{1}{4}n\overline{C}$, where n is the number density and $\overline{C}$ the mean thermal speed. Hence, assuming that in the diffusing gas the thermal motions follow a Maxwellian distribution, the flux of molecules (1) in either direction through unit area of the plane $z=0$, due to the thermal motions, is $\frac{1}{4}n_1\overline{C}_1$. Here n_1 is the number density not at the plane $z=0$ but at a distance $\bar{z}_1$ from this plane, $\bar{z}_1$ being the average distance of transfer of number. Similarly, $\overline{C}_1$ is the mean speed at a distance $\bar{z}_1'$ from the plane $z=0$, $\bar{z}_1'$ being the average distance of transfer of mean speed. The distinction made here between these distances is essential in this theory; it arises when account is taken of the persistence of velocity after collision (cf. Jeans, 1940). Thus if n_1^0, $\overline{C}_1^0$ refer to the plane $z=0$ the flux of molecules (1) in the negative z direction is

$$\frac{1}{4}\left(n_1^0+\frac{\partial n_1}{\partial z}\bar{z}_1\right)\left(\overline{C}_1^0+\frac{\partial \overline{C}_1}{\partial z}\bar{z}_1'\right),$$

and in the positive direction

$$\frac{1}{4}\left(n_1^0-\frac{\partial n_1}{\partial z}\bar{z}_1\right)\left(\overline{C}_1^0-\frac{\partial \overline{C}_1}{\partial z}\bar{z}_1'\right);$$

so that the net flux in the positive direction is approximately

$$\Gamma_1'=-\frac{1}{2}\left[\frac{\partial n_1}{\partial z}\bar{z}_1\overline{C}_1+\frac{\partial \overline{C}_1}{\partial z}\bar{z}_1'n_1\right],$$

and for molecules (2)

$$\Gamma_2'=-\frac{1}{2}\left[\frac{\partial n_2}{\partial z}\bar{z}_2\overline{C}_2+\frac{\partial \overline{C}_2}{\partial z}\bar{z}_2'n_2\right],$$

where the suffix is omitted since the position of the plane $z=0$ is arbitrary.

In general $\Gamma_1'+\Gamma_2'\neq0$, and if uniformity of pressure is to be maintained there must be a motion of the gas as a whole of such a magnitude that there is no net transfer of molecules across the plane. The velocity v of this motion is therefore defined by

$$\Gamma_1'+\Gamma_2'+nv=0, \quad \text{where } n=n_1+n_2,$$

and the total flux density is

$$\Gamma_1 = \Gamma_1' + n_1 v \quad \text{for molecules (1)},$$

and

$$\Gamma_2 = \Gamma_2' + n_2 v \quad \text{for molecules (2)}.$$

Since $\Gamma_1/n_1 = \bar{c}_1$, the mean velocity of molecules (1), and $\Gamma_2/n_2 = \bar{c}_2$, the mean velocity of molecules (2), the diffusion velocity is

$$\bar{c}_1 - \bar{c}_2 = \frac{\Gamma_1}{n_1} - \frac{\Gamma_2}{n_2} = \frac{\Gamma_1'}{n_1} - \frac{\Gamma_2'}{n_2}$$

$$= -\frac{1}{2}\left[\frac{1}{n_1}\frac{\partial n_1}{\partial z}\bar{z}_1 \bar{C}_1 - \frac{1}{n_2}\frac{\partial n_2}{\partial z}\bar{z}_2 \bar{C}_2 + \frac{\partial \bar{C}_1}{\partial z}\bar{z}_1' - \frac{\partial \bar{C}_2}{\partial z}\bar{z}_2'\right].$$

This can be expressed, as shown in Appendix 1, as

$$\bar{c}_1 - \bar{c}_2 = -\frac{D_{12}}{n_{10} n_{20}}\left[\frac{\partial n_{10}}{\partial z} + k_T \frac{1}{T}\frac{\partial T}{\partial z}\right],$$

an equation which is formally identical with the equation of diffusion of Chapman and Enskog (1.2). The coefficient of ordinary diffusion is here given by

$$D_{12} = \tfrac{1}{2}[n_{20}\bar{C}_1\bar{z}_1 + n_{10}\bar{C}_2\bar{z}_2],$$

a formula originally due to Meyer, and the thermal diffusion ratio by

$$k_T = \frac{\left(\bar{z}_1 - \dfrac{\bar{z}_1'}{2}\right)\sqrt{m_2} - \left(\bar{z}_2 - \dfrac{\bar{z}_2'}{2}\right)\sqrt{m_1}}{\bar{z}_1\sqrt{m_2}\,n_{20} + \bar{z}_2\sqrt{m_1}\,n_{10}},$$

where m_1, m_2 are the molecular masses. Making certain reasonable assumptions about the relation of $\bar{z}$ and $\bar{z}'$, Fürth shows that this expression for k_T can be put in a form which corresponds with that of the rigorous theory (cf. §2.10), viz.

$$k_T = \left(1 - \frac{a}{2}\right)\frac{a_1 n_{10} - a_2 n_{20}}{b_1 n_{10}^2 + b_2 n_{20}^2 + b_{12} n_{10} n_{20}} n_{10} n_{20},$$

where the quantity a depends on the relation between $\bar{z}$ and $\bar{z}'$, and therefore on the nature of the intermolecular forces, and $a_1, a_2, b_1, b_2, b_{12}$ are functions of the molecular diameters and masses.

Some of the chief characteristics of thermal diffusion can be deduced from this expression. For example, the first factor $(1 - \tfrac{1}{2}a)$ has a maximum value when the molecules behave as rigid elastic spheres, and it vanishes when $\bar{z}_1/\bar{z}_1' = \bar{z}_2/\bar{z}_2' = 0.5$, which must therefore be regarded as a condition which holds for Maxwellian molecules. Further, the expressions for a_1, a_2 etc. (cf. Appendix 1) show that, provided $(1 - \frac{1}{2}a)$ is positive, k_T is positive for all proportions when the mass m_1 of the molecules of the first kind is greater than the mass m_2 of the second kind. This means that the heavier molecules concentrate in the cooler region. If the molecules have equal masses but different diameters, then it is the larger molecules which concentrate in the cooler region.

This elementary theory thus leads to some formal relations and conclusions which correspond with those of the rigorous theory but, as is to be expected, the correspondence fails in detail. For example, it has long been recognized that the expression for the coefficient of concentration diffusion indicates a much greater variation of D_{12} with the composition than is found experimentally. Furry (1948) has commented upon the inadequacy of theories of this kind, based on the mean free path, especially in treating of diffusion. He considers the approach followed by Frankel mentioned above to be preferable, and has developed this method further, sacrificing, however, to a large extent the elementary character of the theory. For the interpretation of the experimental results the rigorous theory is necessary.

CHAPTER II

THE THEORY OF THERMAL DIFFUSION

The rigorous theory of thermal diffusion is complex. It is fully treated in *The Mathematical Theory of Non-Uniform Gases* by Chapman and Cowling (1939) and in papers by Chapman (1912–40), Clark Jones (1940, 1941) and others. Although no adequate account of the theory can be presented here, an outline must be given of the nature of the problem and its solution; this is necessary to an understanding of the significance of the experimental results to be described later.

2.1. The non-uniform state

The state of a gas may be described by giving the number of molecules (of each kind if there is more than one) per unit volume which have velocities within each of the various ranges. If the molecular velocity c has components u, v, w, a small range of velocity about c is represented by the volume element in velocity-space du, dv, dw. Chapman denotes this element by dc (to be distinguished from $d\mathbf{c}$, which is an element of the vector $\mathbf{c}$) and a range dc about the value c is conveniently referred to as the range c, dc or more briefly as the range dc. Using dr to denote in the same way the volume element dx, dy, dz in configuration space, the number of molecules in the element dr about the point $\mathbf{r}$ (that is, in the element $\mathbf{r}, dr$) with velocities in the range c, dc is $f dc\, dr$, where f is the distribution function.

In general, the velocity distribution may vary from point to point within the gas, and also from instant to instant; the distribution function therefore involves, in general, the position vector $\mathbf{r}$, and the time t as well as the velocity c. This is the case, for example, if there is a relative motion or a temperature difference between different parts of the gas. Whatever its initial state a gas will, in the absence of external influences, undergo changes which bring it ultimately into a state of equilibrium; the decay of internal motions is attributed to viscosity, of temperature differences to thermal conductivity, and of differences in composition to diffusion. In this equilibrium state the distribution function is independent both of position and time; that is, $\partial f/\partial \mathbf{r} = \partial f/\partial t = 0$. It is only for this state of complete equilibrium that the distribution function is readily determined. By methods based on kinetic theory or on statistical mechanics it can be shown to have the well-known Maxwellian form

$$f = n\left(\frac{m}{2\pi kT}\right)^{\frac{3}{2}} \exp\left[-\frac{mC^2}{2kT}\right],$$

where n is the number density, m the mass, C the thermal velocity of the molecules. In addition to this state, others are possible in which the distribution function is independent of either position or time. If the former, $\partial f/\partial \mathbf{r} = 0$, and the state is uniform; if the latter, $\partial f/\partial t = 0$, and the state is steady.

The study of transport phenomena is concerned with gases which, although they may be in a steady state, are not in a uniform state. It calls therefore for a knowledge of the distribution function for non-uniform gases, and this involves the solution of the Boltzmann equation in its general form.

2.2. Boltzmann's equation

Consider two groups of molecules in a gas. The first consists of those molecules which occupy a volume $d\mathbf{r}$ about the point $\mathbf{r}$ and whose velocities are within the range $\mathbf{c}, d\mathbf{c}$ at the instant t. The number in this group is then $f(\mathbf{r}, \mathbf{c}, t)\,d\mathbf{r}\,d\mathbf{c}$. The second group consists of those molecules in volume $d\mathbf{r}$ about the point $(\mathbf{r} + \mathbf{c}\,dt)$ with velocities in the range $\mathbf{c}, d\mathbf{c}$ at the instant $t + dt$. The number in this second group is $f(\mathbf{r} + \mathbf{c}\,dt, \mathbf{c}, t + dt)\,d\mathbf{r}\,d\mathbf{c}$. Since, in the absence of external forces, a molecule of the first group moves through a distance $\mathbf{c}\,dt$ in time dt provided it makes no collision, it follows that, if there were no collisions, the second group would comprise exactly the same molecules as the first and no others, and the numbers in the two groups would be identical. When collisions occur, however, some molecules of the first group do not appear in the second, since they undergo deflexions during the interval dt; and the second group includes molecules which are not present in the first but which are deflected into it in the interval dt. The numbers in the two groups are therefore in general different. Let the difference, which is a measure of the effect of collisions on the distribution function, be denoted by

$$\frac{\partial_e f}{\partial t}\, d\mathbf{r}\, d\mathbf{c}\, dt,$$

since it must be proportional to $d\mathbf{r}\, d\mathbf{c}\, dt$. Then

$$\frac{\partial_e f}{\partial t}\, dt = f(\mathbf{r}+\mathbf{c}\, dt, \mathbf{c}, t+dt) - f(\mathbf{r}, \mathbf{c}, t),$$

and in the limit, as $dt \to 0$,

$$\frac{\partial_e f}{\partial t} = \mathbf{c} \cdot \frac{\partial f}{\partial \mathbf{r}} + \frac{\partial f}{\partial t}, \qquad (2.1)$$

where $\partial f/\partial \mathbf{r}$ represents the gradient of f, with components $\partial f/\partial x$, $\partial f/\partial y$, $\partial f/\partial z$. This is Boltzmann's equation. Before it can be solved the effect of collisions, represented by $\partial_e f/\partial t$, must be evaluated.

To determine the effect of collisions on the distribution function we will suppose, for generality, that the gas consists of molecules of two kinds, the distribution functions being f_1 and f_2. Consider first those molecules of the first kind only in the volume $d\mathbf{r}$, and the change in their number in the interval dt which results from collisions between molecules of the first kind with molecules of the second kind only. Let A be a molecule of the first kind moving with velocity $\mathbf{c}_1$ and B be a molecule of the second kind with velocity $\mathbf{c}_2$, and suppose the molecules interact with a force which depends only on the distance between them and which is directed along the line joining them. Considering the motion of B relative to A by referring the motion to axes through A, let B be moving initially asymptotically to $P_1 P_2$ (fig. 6). The path of B then lies in a plane through A containing $P_1 P_2$. The point of closest approach to A is M. AM cuts $P_1 P_2$ at O. The motion after the encounter is then asymptotic to OQ, and the deflexion produced is $\chi = P_2 \hat{O} Q$; the velocities are now $\mathbf{c}_1'$ and $\mathbf{c}_2'$. The angle of deflexion χ depends in general on the relative velocity $\mathbf{g} = \mathbf{c}_2 - \mathbf{c}_1$, and on the distance b of A from OP_1 or OQ. The orientation of the plane containing the path is specified by the angle ϵ between this plane and another containing AP' (AP' is parallel to OP_1) and a fixed direction.

It follows that the number of encounters of the type considered which occur in time dt and involve the molecule A is given by the number of molecules of the second kind with velocity $\mathbf{c}_2$ which lie in a right prism of height $g\,dt$ and base the element of area $dS = b\,db\,d\epsilon$ in the plane through A perpendicular to AP'. This number is

$$f_2(\mathbf{c}_2)\,d\mathbf{c}_2 g b\,db\,d\epsilon\,dt.$$

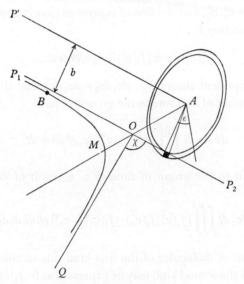

Fig. 6. A molecular encounter.

Hence in a group of molecules in volume $d\mathbf{r}$ of the gas the total number of encounters of this type between a molecule of the first kind and one of the second kind in time dt is

$$f_1(\mathbf{c}_1)\,d\mathbf{r}\,d\mathbf{c}_1 f_2(\mathbf{c}_2)\,d\mathbf{c}_2 g b\,db\,d\epsilon\,dt;$$

and the number of encounters made by molecules of the first kind with molecules of the second kind, whatever their velocity, is found by integrating the above expression over all values of $\mathbf{c}_2$, b and ϵ; this number is therefore

$$d\mathbf{r}\,d\mathbf{c}_1\,dt \iiint f_1(\mathbf{c}_1) f_2(\mathbf{c}_2)\,d\mathbf{c}_2 g b\,db\,d\epsilon.$$

Each encounter changes the velocity of the molecule and therefore causes it to leave the group. Conversely, during the time dt the group will gain members as a result of collisions between molecules of the first and second kinds which leave the former with velocity c_1. It can be shown that for this to happen the molecules must have initial velocities equal to the final velocities of the previous case and approach each other in such a way that the line joining them at closest approach is now in the reverse direction. The number of entrants to the group resulting from collisions in which the initial velocities are c_1', c_2', and the line of centres at closest approach is in a specific direction is

$$f_1(c_1')\, dr\, dc_1' f_2(c_2')\, dc_2' gb\, db\, d\epsilon\, dt.$$

A further argument shows that $dc_1'\, dc_2' = dc_1\, dc_2$, and therefore for the total number of entrants to the group we have

$$dr\, dc_1\, dt \int\!\!\int\!\!\int f_1(c_1') f_2(c_2')\, dc_2 gb\, db\, d\epsilon\, dt.$$

The net gain to the group in time dt as a result of collisions is therefore

$$dr\, dc_1\, dt \int\!\!\int\!\!\int [f_1(c_1') f_2(c_2') - f_1(c_1) f_2(c_2)]\, gb\, db\, d\epsilon\, dc_2.$$

This net gain of molecules of the first kind due to collisions with molecules of the second kind may be expressed as $(\partial_e f_1/\partial t)_2\, dr\, dc_1\, dt$. Hence

$$\left(\frac{\partial_e f_1}{\partial t}\right)_2 = \int\!\!\int\!\!\int [f_1(c_1') f_2(c_2') - f_1(c_1) f_2(c_2)]\, gb\, db\, d\epsilon\, dc_2;$$

and for the total rate of change of f_1 there must be added to this a similar expression representing the increment due to collisions in which both molecules are of the first kind. Thus Boltzmann's equation becomes

$$\frac{\partial_e f_1}{\partial t} = \left(\frac{\partial_e f_1}{\partial t}\right)_1 + \left(\frac{\partial_e f_1}{\partial t}\right)_2 \equiv \Sigma \int\!\!\int\!\!\int [f_1(c_1') f_2(c_2') - f_1(c_1) f_2(c_2)]\, gb\, db\, d\epsilon\, dc_2$$

$$= c \cdot \frac{\partial f_1}{\partial r} + \frac{\partial f_1}{\partial t}, \qquad (2.2)$$

and there is a similar equation for f_2.

2.3. The solution of Boltzmann's equation

For a gas in its equilibrium state, Boltzmann's equation is readily solved, for in this special case it reduces to

$$\frac{\partial_e f}{\partial t} = 0, \quad \text{since} \quad \frac{\partial f}{\partial \mathbf{r}} = \frac{\partial f}{\partial t} = 0.$$

Considering for simplicity a simple gas consisting of molecules of one kind only, we obtain therefore

$$\iiint [f(\mathbf{c}_1')f(\mathbf{c}_2') - f(\mathbf{c}_1)f(\mathbf{c}_2)] gb\, db\, d\epsilon\, d\mathbf{c}_2 = 0,$$

which clearly has a solution

$$f(\mathbf{c}_1')f(\mathbf{c}_2') = f(\mathbf{c}_1)f(\mathbf{c}_2),$$

or
$$\log f(\mathbf{c}_1') + \log f(\mathbf{c}_2') = \log f(\mathbf{c}_1) + \log f(\mathbf{c}_2).$$

$\log f$ is thus a summational invariant for the collision. This suggests that $\log f$ is a linear combination of those mechanical quantities—energy, momentum—which are conserved in the encounter. On this basis the distribution function is found to have the familiar Maxwellian form already quoted.

In the general case, however, when the gas is in neither a steady nor a uniform state, the general equation

$$\frac{\partial_e f}{\partial t} = \mathbf{c} \cdot \frac{\partial f}{\partial \mathbf{r}} + \frac{\partial f}{\partial t}$$

must be solved.

Enskog obtained a solution by a method of successive approximations. In a gas at normal densities, collisions are by far the most important factor affecting f; hence a first approximation to f is $f^{(0)}$, where $f^{(0)}$ is the value of f given by $\partial_e f/\partial t = 0$; thus $f^{(0)}$ is the Maxwellian function. A second approximation is $f = f^{(0)} + f^{(1)}$, where $f^{(1)}$ is small; in substituting this expression for f in Boltzmann's equation, products of two functions $f^{(1)}$ are neglected in $\partial_e f/\partial t$, and $f^{(1)}$ is neglected completely in $\mathbf{c} \cdot \partial f/\partial \mathbf{r} + \partial f/\partial t$. Thus $f_1^{(1)}$ and $f_2^{(1)}$ are found from

$$\frac{\partial f_1^{(0)}}{\partial t} + \mathbf{c}_1 \cdot \frac{\partial f_1^{(0)}}{\partial \mathbf{r}} = \Sigma \iiint [f_1^{(0)}(\mathbf{c}_1')f_2^{(1)}(\mathbf{c}_2') + f_1^{(1)}(\mathbf{c}_1')f_2^{(0)}(\mathbf{c}_2') - f_1^{(0)}(\mathbf{c}_1)f_2^{(1)}(\mathbf{c}_2)$$
$$- f_1^{(1)}(\mathbf{c}_1)f_2^{(0)}(\mathbf{c}_2)] gb\, db\, d\epsilon\, d\mathbf{c}_1,$$

and a similar equation. Further approximations $f^{(0)} + f^{(1)} + f^{(2)} \ldots$ to f can also be obtained; but for normal gases it is usually sufficient to confine attention to the second approximation $f^{(0)} + f^{(1)}$.

Without solving the equation for $f^{(1)}$, some inferences can be made about the nature of this function in a gas which is at rest. In such a gas $\partial f_1^{(0)}/\partial t$ is negligibly small compared with $\mathbf{c}_1 \cdot \partial f_1^{(0)}/\partial \mathbf{r}$; also, if the gas is to remain at rest the pressure must be uniform. Hence the only quantities which can vary with position are the composition and temperature, and the left-hand side of the equation for $f^{(1)}$ must be a linear function of $\partial n_{10}/\partial \mathbf{r}$ ($\equiv -\partial n_{20}/\partial \mathbf{r}$) and $\partial T/\partial \mathbf{r}$. Since the functions $f^{(1)}$ appear linearly on the right of this equation, it follows that these functions involve $\partial n_{10}/\partial \mathbf{r}$ and $\partial T/\partial \mathbf{r}$ linearly.

2.4. The diffusion velocity and the thermal flux

From the forms of the functions $f^{(1)}$, formal expressions for the thermal flux and the velocity of diffusion can be derived. The diffusion velocity, that is the difference between the mean velocities, or mean thermal velocities, of the two kinds of molecule, is

$$\bar{\mathbf{C}}_1 - \bar{\mathbf{C}}_2 = \frac{1}{n_1} \int f_1 \mathbf{C}_1 \, d\mathbf{c}_1 - \frac{1}{n_2} \int f_2 \mathbf{C}_2 \, d\mathbf{c}_2$$

$$= \frac{1}{n_1} \int (f_1^{(0)} + f_1^{(1)}) \, \mathbf{C}_1 \, d\mathbf{c}_1 - \frac{1}{n_2} \int (f_2^{(0)} + f_2^{(1)}) \, \mathbf{C}_2 \, d\mathbf{c}_2$$

$$= \frac{1}{n_1} \int f_1^{(1)} \mathbf{C}_1 \, d\mathbf{c}_1 - \frac{1}{n_2} \int f_2^{(1)} \mathbf{C}_2 \, d\mathbf{c}_2,$$

the integrals involving $f^{(0)}$ vanishing. Since the functions $f^{(1)}$ are linear in $\partial n_{10}/\partial \mathbf{r}$ and $\partial T/\partial \mathbf{r}$, it follows that $\bar{\mathbf{C}}_1 - \bar{\mathbf{C}}_2$ is of the form

$$\bar{\mathbf{C}}_1 - \bar{\mathbf{C}}_2 = -\frac{D_{12}}{n_{10} n_{20}} \left[\frac{\partial n_{10}}{\partial \mathbf{r}} + \frac{k_T}{T} \frac{\partial T}{\partial \mathbf{r}} \right], \qquad (2.3)$$

with appropriate values for D_{12} and k_T.

An expression for the flux density of molecules through a surface stationary with respect to the gas follows immediately. For molecules of the first kind this flux is $\mathbf{\Gamma}_1 = n_1 \bar{\mathbf{C}}_1$. Since $n_1 \bar{\mathbf{C}}_1 + n_2 \bar{\mathbf{C}}_2 = 0$,

$$\bar{\mathbf{C}}_1 - \bar{\mathbf{C}}_2 = \bar{\mathbf{C}}_1 (1 + n_1/n_2) = (n/n_2) \bar{\mathbf{C}}_1,$$

and therefore $n_1 \bar{\mathbf{C}}_1 = \dfrac{n_1 n_2}{n} (\bar{\mathbf{C}}_1 - \bar{\mathbf{C}}_2).$

Hence
$$\mathbf{\Gamma}_1 = -nD_{12}\left[\frac{\partial n_{10}}{\partial \mathbf{r}} + k_T \frac{1}{T}\frac{\partial T}{\partial \mathbf{r}}\right].\qquad(2.4)$$

(This equation, without the term involving the temperature gradient, is often made the basis of the definition of the coefficient of concentration diffusion.)

For the thermal flux in a gas consisting of one kind of molecule only we have

$$\mathbf{q} = \int \tfrac{1}{2}mC^2 f\mathbf{C}\,d\mathbf{c},$$

or
$$\mathbf{q} = \int \tfrac{1}{2}mC^2 f^{(0)}\mathbf{C}\,d\mathbf{c} + \int \tfrac{1}{2}mC^2 f^{(1)}\mathbf{C}\,d\mathbf{c}$$

$$= \int \tfrac{1}{2}mC^2 f^{(1)}\mathbf{C}\,d\mathbf{c},$$

since the first integral vanishes. The function $f^{(1)}$ being linear in $\partial T/\partial \mathbf{r}$, the expression for the flux is of the form

$$\mathbf{q} = -\lambda\,\partial T/\partial \mathbf{r},\qquad(2.5)$$

where λ is the coefficient of thermal conductivity. When the mixture contains two kinds of molecule the thermal flux is

$$\mathbf{q} = \int \tfrac{1}{2}m_1 C_1^2 f_1^{(1)}\mathbf{C}_1\,d\mathbf{c}_1 + \int \tfrac{1}{2}m_2 C_2^2 f_2^{(1)}\mathbf{C}_2\,d\mathbf{c}_2.$$

Here the functions $f^{(1)}$ are linear in both $\partial T/\partial \mathbf{r}$ and $\partial n_{10}/\partial \mathbf{r}$, or from the above equations for $(\bar{\mathbf{C}}_1 - \bar{\mathbf{C}}_2)$, in $\partial T/\partial \mathbf{r}$ and $(\bar{\mathbf{C}}_1 - \bar{\mathbf{C}}_2)$, and the expression for $\mathbf{q}$ takes the form

$$\mathbf{q} = -\lambda\,\partial T/\partial \mathbf{r} + nkTk_T(\bar{\mathbf{C}}_1 - \bar{\mathbf{C}}_2).\qquad(2.6)$$

The first term represents a heat transport by conduction, the second a transport due to diffusion.

The equations for $\bar{\mathbf{C}}_1 - \bar{\mathbf{C}}_2$ and $\mathbf{q}$ have been derived for a gas at rest; but they apply also to a gas in motion, provided that the motion introduces no large pressure gradients, $\mathbf{q}$ denoting the flow of heat relative to the gas.

Explicit expressions for D_{12}, λ and k_T can be found only if $f_1^{(1)}$ and $f_2^{(1)}$ are known. Exact expressions for these cannot in general be found; normally only a crude first approximation to their values is obtained. This first approximation gives values of D_{12}, λ and k_T which may be appreciably lower than the correct ones. The error is likely to be greatest for k_T; its actual value, however, is difficult to assess, save in certain special cases.

2.5. The collision integrals

The expressions for the coefficients derived in this way all involve one or more integrals which are functions of those quantities—the relative velocity $\mathbf{g}$, the deflexion χ, and the parameter b—which define a molecular collision. For the interaction of molecules of different kinds $(1, 2)$, the collision integrals are of the type

$$\Omega_{12}^{(l)}(r) = \pi^{\frac{1}{2}} \int_0^\infty \epsilon^{-\gamma^2} \gamma^{2r+2} \phi^{(l)} d\gamma,$$

where $\quad \gamma = \left[\dfrac{m_1 m_2}{(m_1+m_2)\, 2kT} \right]^{\frac{1}{2}} g, \quad \phi^{(l)} = \int (1 - \cos^l \chi) gb\, db,$

and l and r are small integers. The integrals can be evaluated only when the law of interaction of the molecules is known, for on this depends the relation between χ, b and g. In dealing with a gas mixture there are three types of interaction to be considered, two involving like molecules $(1, 1)$ and $(2, 2)$, and one involving unlike molecules $(1, 2)$. In general, the molecular mass ratios and the law of force will be different in each, and the appropriate collision integrals must be distinguished—thus we write $\Omega_1^{(l)}(r), \Omega_2^{(l)}(r), \Omega_{12}^{(l)}(r)$. $\Omega_1^{(l)}(r)$ is derived from $\Omega_{12}^{(l)}(r)$ by writing m_1 for m_2; similarly for $\Omega_2^{(l)}(r)$.

As examples, the coefficients of viscosity, μ, and conductivity, λ, of a simple gas may be cited. They are, in first approximation, respectively

$$[\mu]_1 = \frac{5kT}{8\Omega_1^{(2)}(2)} \quad \text{and} \quad [\lambda]_1 = \frac{25c_v kT}{16\Omega_1^{(2)}(2)}. \tag{2.7}$$

(c_v = specific heat at constant volume.) For the coefficient of ordinary (concentration) diffusion in a gas mixture we obtain

$$D_{12} = \frac{3}{2nm_0} \frac{kT}{8M_1 M_2 \Omega_{12}^{(1)}(1)}, \tag{2.8}$$

where $m_0 = m_1 + m_2$ and $M_1 = m_1/m_0$, $M_2 = m_2/m_0$. The coefficient of thermal diffusion D_T and the ratio $k_T = D_T/D_{12}$ involve more complex expressions which are given later.

The evaluation of these integrals is itself a major mathematical problem, and it is only for a few simple modes of interaction that it has been done. The chief cases which have been treated so far are:

(i) molecules which behave as rigid elastic spheres;

(ii) molecules which exert a repulsive force F which varies inversely as the νth power of the distance r, i.e. $F = \kappa r^{-\nu}$, where κ is the force constant;

(iii) molecules which exert an inverse power attraction superposed on an inverse power repulsion, so that the resultant force is

$$F = \kappa r^{-\nu} - \kappa' r^{-\nu'},$$

where κ and ν refer to the repulsive force, κ' and ν' to the attractive force.

Lennard-Jones has used the third model extensively in explaining various properties of gases and solids; it will be referred to therefore as the Lennard-Jones model. The well-known Sutherland model, which represents a molecule as a rigid sphere of diameter σ surrounded by a field of attraction varying inversely as a power of the distance, may be regarded as a special case of the Lennard-Jones model. It corresponds with $\nu = \infty$ and a value of κ such that the repulsive force is zero for $r > \sigma$ and infinite for $r < \sigma$. The integrals for the Sutherland model and for the case when ν is arbitrary and $\nu' = 3$ have been given by Chapman and Cowling ($M.T.$ pp. 180–7). More recently the special cases of $\nu = 9$, $\nu' = 5$ and $\nu = 13$, $\nu' = 7$ have been treated.

Isotopic mixtures and Lorentzian mixtures. There are two types of mixture for which the theory is less complex than in the general case. The first is that of a mixture in which the interactions of like and of unlike molecules accord with the same law; in this case the collision integrals differ only because of the different molecular masses, and a simple relation exists between them (cf. §2.7). Such mixtures Chapman describes as isotopic, since a mixture of isotopes falls into this class. Secondly, there is the case of a mixture in which the mass of one species is very large compared with that of the other, and at the same time either the proportion of the heavier species or its relative size is very large; that is, when

$$m_1/m_2 \to \infty, \quad \text{and either} \quad n_{10} \to 1 \text{ or } \sigma_1/\sigma_2 \to \infty.$$

Here the only interactions which have to be considered are of the (1, 2) type, the others being relatively infrequent, and a much simpler treatment is possible than in the general case. Exact values for the transport coefficients can be found, and thus an estimate may be made of the error of the approximations of the general theory. This case was studied by Lorentz; Chapman therefore terms a mixture in which these conditions hold a *Lorentzian* gas.

2.6. The thermal diffusion ratio and the thermal diffusion factor

In the expressions for the thermal diffusion ratio k_T the integrals appear as ratios. Five such are involved:

$$A = \frac{\Omega_{12}^{(2)}(2)}{5\Omega_{12}^{(1)}(1)}, \quad B = \frac{5\Omega_{12}^{(1)}(2) - \Omega_{12}^{(1)}(3)}{5\Omega_{12}^{(1)}(1)}, \quad C = \frac{2\Omega_{12}^{(1)}(2)}{5\Omega_{12}^{(1)}(1)},$$
$$E_1 = \frac{2\Omega_1^{(2)}(2)}{5(1-M)\Omega_{12}^{(1)}(1)}, \quad E_2 = \frac{2\Omega_2^{(2)}(2)}{5(1+M)\Omega_{12}^{(1)}(1)}, \quad (2.9)$$

where M is the proportionate mass difference $(m_1 - m_2)/(m_1 + m_2)$. Of these ratios A, B and C depend only on the temperature and on the law of interaction of unlike molecules, i.e. interactions (1, 2). E_1 and E_2 depend on the temperature, on the ratio of the molecular masses and on the law of interaction of both like and unlike molecules.

In terms of these ratios the first approximation to the thermal diffusion ratio is

$$[k_T]_1 = 5(C - 1) \frac{S_1 n_{10} - S_2 n_{20}}{Q_1 n_{10}^2 + Q_2 n_{20}^2 + Q_{12} n_{10} n_{20}} n_{10} n_{20}, \quad (2.10)$$

where n_{10}, n_{20} are the volume fractions of the two components and the quantities S, Q are functions of the ratios A, B, E_1, E_2 and of the molecular masses m_1, m_2. If

$$M_1 = \frac{m_1}{m_1 + m_2}, \quad M_2 = \frac{m_2}{m_1 + m_2},$$

and $M = M_1 - M_2$, the proportionate mass difference, then

$$S_1 = M_1 E_1 - 4AM_1 M_2 - 3M_2(M_2 - M_1),$$
$$Q_1 = E_1[6M_2^2 + (5 - 4B)M_1^2 + 8M_1 M_2 A],$$
$$Q_{12} = 3(M_1 - M_2)^2(5 - 4B) + 4M_1 M_2 A(11 - 4B) + 2E_1 E_2, \quad (2.11)$$

with relations for S_2, Q_2 derived from S_1, Q_1 by interchange of subscripts.

From the occurrence in this expression of the product $n_{10}n_{20}$ it is obvious that k_T is strongly dependent on the relative proportions of the components; it is convenient therefore to introduce the thermal diffusion factor α defined as $k_T/n_{10}n_{20}$, and given in first approximation by

$$[\alpha]_1 = 5(C-1)\frac{S_1 n_{10} - S_2 n_{20}}{Q_1 n_{10}^2 + Q_2 n_{20}^2 + Q_{12} n_{10} n_{20}}. \qquad (2.12)$$

The thermal diffusion factor is still dependent on the relative proportions but to a much less extent than is k_T. If α were independent of the concentration, the curve showing the variation of k_T with concentration would be a parabola with vertex at $n_{10} = n_{20} = 0\cdot5$. The experimental curves approximate to this form when the mass ratio is small, but otherwise depart noticeably from it (cf. fig. 3). The factor α therefore varies appreciably with composition, as may be expected, but much less rapidly than does k_T.

The factor $5(C-1)$ appearing in $[k_T]_1$ and $[\alpha]_1$ depends only on the law of interaction of unlike molecules and on the temperature; it is independent of the mass ratio and of the composition. When the molecules interact according to an inverse power repulsion, the force between unlike molecules at distance r being $F = \kappa_{12} r^{-\nu_{12}}$,

$$5(C-1) = \frac{\nu_{12}-5}{\nu_{12}-1}.$$

Hence $[k_T]_1$, and also the exact value k_T, is zero always if the force index $\nu_{12} = 5$; it is positive for $\nu_{12} > 5$, and negative for $\nu_{12} < 5$. The maximum value of this factor is unity, which occurs for $\nu_{12} = \infty$, i.e. for molecules which behave like rigid spheres.

Of the remaining factor the quantities Q_1 and Q_2 are essentially positive, and Q_{12} is positive probably for all physically suitable molecular models, and certainly for molecules which exert an inverse power repulsion. The signs of S_1 and S_2 depend in a complex manner on the mass ratios and the nature of the interactions. For mixtures in which the mass difference is large and positive, S_1 is positive, S_2 is negative, so that k_T is positive at all compositions (assuming, as we do henceforth, that $5(C-1)$ is positive). This means that the heavier molecules (1) diffuse down the temperature gradient. This is what is usually observed. However, when the mass difference is small, the extension of the molecular fields becomes the dominating factor. Then, if the heavier molecule is the smaller, contrary to the usual condition, S_1 may be negative and S_2 positive; in this case k_T has a negative value, and the heavier molecule diffuses up the temperature gradient. Or S_1 and S_2 may be of the same sign, implying a change in the sign of k_T at some particular concentration. Such a reversal of sign has been observed in neon-ammonia mixtures (cf. Chapter v).

2.7. Theoretical values of the thermal diffusion factor

We consider now the values found for the thermal diffusion factor in those cases for which the necessary integrations have been performed.

The thermal diffusion factor can be evaluated simply only for the isotopic case, for here the integrals appropriate to the interaction of like and unlike molecules differ by a factor which depends only on the molecular masses. For non-isotopic mixtures the relations are complex. For the isotopic case the collision integrals are related thus:

$$\left(\frac{m_1}{2}\right)^{\frac{1}{2}}\Omega_1 = \left(\frac{m_1 m_2}{m_1 + m_2}\right)^{\frac{1}{2}}\Omega_{12} = \left(\frac{m_2}{2}\right)^{\frac{1}{2}}\Omega_2. \qquad (2.13)$$

Hence the quantities E_1, E_2 in the expression for $[\alpha]_1$ become

$$E_1 = \frac{2A}{(1-M)^{\frac{1}{2}}}, \qquad E_2 = \frac{2A}{(1+M)^{\frac{1}{2}}}.$$

When the molecules are rigid elastic spheres, however, the calculation of $[\alpha]_1$ is still relatively simple even when the diameters of the two species of molecules are different. The only quantities affected are E_1 and E_2; these now have the values above multiplied respectively by $(\sigma_1/\sigma_{12})^2$ and $(\sigma_2/\sigma_{12})^2$, where σ_1, σ_2 are the diameters of the two species and σ_{12} is the mean diameter $\frac{1}{2}(\sigma_1 + \sigma_2)$.

If the mixture is not only isotopic but one in which the mass difference M is small (usually the case for mixtures of isotopes), the expression (2.12) can be simplified. A series expansion for $[k_T]_1$ or $[\alpha]_1$ in powers of M is then possible (cf. Chapman, 1940b), the first term for the thermal diffusion factor being

$$[\alpha]_1 = \alpha_0[1 - \gamma M(n_{10} - n_{20})], \qquad (2.14)$$

where

$$\alpha_0 = M.5(C-1)\frac{3\left(1+\dfrac{1}{A}\right)}{(11-4B+8A)},$$

and

$$\gamma = \frac{3(1-\frac{1}{2}A)}{2(1+A)} - \frac{2(1+4B)}{(11-4B+8A)}.$$

Thus to a first approximation $[\alpha]_1$ is independent of concentration.

Rigid elastic spheres. Values of the ratios $A, B, C,$ have been given by Chapman and Cowling (cf. *M.T.* p. 172 and Chapman (1940b)).

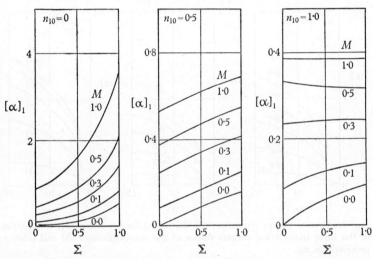

Fig. 7. Rigid elastic spheres: the thermal diffusion factor as a function of the proportionate diameter difference for various values of the mass difference M and relative proportions, n_{10}.

The values of the thermal diffusion factor calculated from them are shown as a function of the proportionate diameter difference Σ in fig. 7. Σ is defined as $(\sigma_1 - \sigma_2)/(\sigma_1 + \sigma_2)$, where σ_1, σ_2 are the molecular diameters. The range of Σ in practice is small and the curves are restricted to $\Sigma = 0 \rightarrow 0.5$. Some details of the calculation are given in Appendix 2. In this case the thermal diffusion factor is independent of temperature.

For mixtures of molecules of the same diameter and nearly the same mass the approximate expression (2.14) gives

$$[\alpha]_1 = \tfrac{105}{118}M = 0.89M.$$

Centres of inverse power repulsion. For isotopic molecules which repel each other with a force $F = \kappa r^{-\nu}$, the collision integrals are again independent of temperature. Their values and those of the ratios A, B, C for various assigned values of the force index have been given by Chapman (1940*b*). They are reproduced in Appendix 2. Values of the thermal diffusion factor, $[\alpha]_1$, calculated from them for various values of the mass difference M are shown in fig. 8. The values for $\nu = \infty$ correspond with those above for rigid spheres of equal diameter.

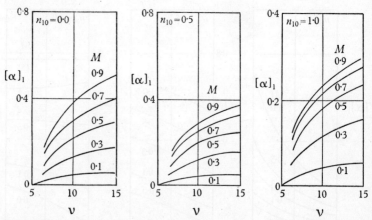

Fig. 8. Inverse power repulsion: the thermal diffusion factor $[\alpha]_1$ as function of the force index ν for various values of the mass difference M and relative proportions, n_{10}.

The general increase of $[\alpha]_1$ with increasing force index is apparent. It is clear too that the thermal diffusion factor decreases as the proportion of the heavier molecules increases; the rate of change, however, depends on the mass differences M being small when M is small.

The characteristics of the thermal diffusion factor in this case have been discussed at length by Chapman (1940*b*).

The Lennard-Jones model. In this model the intermolecular force F is represented by

$$F = \kappa r^{-\nu} - \kappa' r^{-\nu'}.$$

The results differ from those preceding in that the quantities A, B, C, E_1 and E_2 and consequently the thermal diffusion factor α are now functions of the temperature. As will be seen, experiments show that in most cases α is dependent on the temperature, decreasing with the temperature. This is the variation given by theoretical results. On first consideration, as Clark Jones (1941) pointed out, this model might be expected to lead to the opposite conclusion. For, considering the simple inverse power model for which $F = \kappa r^{-\nu}$, the force index

$$\nu = \frac{d(\ln F)}{d(\ln r)}.$$

The ratio $d(\ln F)/d(\ln r)$ Clark Jones calls the hardness function $\mu(\nu)$. For the Lennard-Jones model the hardness function is

$$\mu(\nu) = \nu + Q(\nu - \nu') + O(Q^2),$$

where $Q = (\kappa'/\kappa) r^{(\nu - \nu')}$. For values of r less than that at which the potential energy is a minimum, Q is positive and less than unity, so that $\mu(\nu) > \nu$, and by an amount which decreases as r decreases, that is, as the temperature increases. The molecule thus apparently becomes softer as the temperature increases, implying a decrease of α with increasing temperature. The detailed calculations show that this is indeed the case at very high temperatures, but that in the range of temperature to which the experiments are usually restricted the effect of the attractive field is to cause α to decrease with decreasing temperature.

Clark Jones considered in detail the special case $\nu = 9$, $\nu' = 5$—conveniently denoted as the $(9, 5)$ case. As he appreciated, these values of the force indices are not the most probable, but much of the laborious numerical work had been done previously for this case by Hassé and Cook (1929), and Clark Jones therefore extended it to apply to thermal diffusion, since it seemed likely that the results would not differ essentially from those obtained with more suitable indices.

For this model, Clark Jones showed that it is possible, for isotopic mixtures at least, to express α as a function of a quantity kT/ϵ, $-\epsilon$ being the potential energy of two molecules at the equilibrium separation, that is, where attraction changes to repulsion. In terms of the force constants

$$\epsilon = \frac{(\nu - \nu')}{(\nu - 1)(\nu' - 1)} \frac{\kappa'^{\{(\nu - 1)/(\nu - \nu')\}}}{\kappa^{\{(\nu' - 1)/(\nu - \nu')\}}}.$$

As kT/ϵ is roughly equivalent to T/T_c, where T_c is the critical temperature, this means that at the same reduced temperature T/T_c, α has the same value for all isotopic mixtures whatever the force constants κ, κ', provided the force indices are the same (it is assumed here that the mass difference is always small). The arresting feature of the results is the marked dependence of α on the temperature. As the temperature falls from high values,

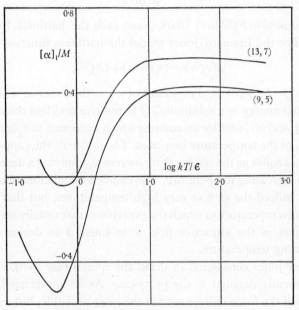

Fig. 9. Lennard-Jones model; $[\alpha]_1/M$ as a function of $\log kT/\epsilon$ for $M < 0\cdot 1$ for the $(13, 7)$ and $(9, 5)$ cases.

α increases slightly until a temperature about $10 T_c$ is attained. Thereafter, α decreases rapidly, becoming negative at about $1\cdot 5 T_c$ and reaching a maximum negative value at about $0\cdot 5 T_c$. This variation is shown graphically in fig. 9.

Recently, Hirschfelder, Bird and Spotz (1948) have treated the case in which the potential energy of interaction of two molecules at distance r apart is given by

$$E(r) = 4\epsilon \left[\left(\frac{\sigma}{r} \right)^{12} - \left(\frac{\sigma}{r} \right)^{6} \right],$$

where $-\epsilon$ is again the minimum potential energy, and σ is the separation at which the energy is zero. This implies force indices $\nu = 13$, $\nu' = 7$ and a relation between the constants: $\kappa = 2\sigma^6 . \kappa'$. This particular case of the Lennard-Jones model has been remarkably successful in accounting for the equation of state and other properties of many gases. From the values of the quantities A, B, C tabulated by Hirschfelder, Bird and Spotz, values of the thermal diffusion factor $[\alpha]_1$ have been calculated for isotopic mixtures of

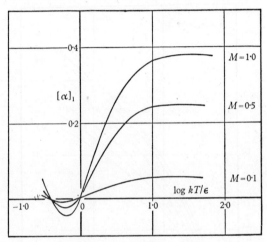

Fig. 10. Lennard-Jones model: $[\alpha]_1$ as a function of $\log kT/\epsilon$ for various values of M when $n_{10} = 0.5$; for the $(13, 7)$ case.

various mass ratios: they are given in Appendix 2, Table III A, and some are shown graphically in fig. 10. The marked dependence of $[\alpha]_1$ on the temperature, first brought out in Clark Jones's work with the $(9, 5)$ model, appears again in the $(13, 7)$ case, but with interesting differences. For the $(13, 7)$ model the value of kT/ϵ at which $[\alpha]_1$ changes sign, and the range over which $[\alpha]_1$ is negative are smaller than for the $(9, 5)$ model, whereas the minimum value of $[\alpha]_1$ is (algebraically) greater.

2.8 The thermal separation ratio R_T

In the discussion of experimental results there has been introduced a quantity denoted by R_T and termed the thermal separation ratio. R_T as determined experimentally is the ratio of the value of k_T or of α (calculated from the measured separation) to the corresponding theoretical value, in first approximation, for molecules which have the same mass and diameter as the experimental ones but which interact like rigid spheres. The diameters are those calculated from the experimental values of the viscosity of the components using expressions appropriate to rigid spheres. Thus

$$R_T(\text{exp.}) = \frac{k_T(\text{exp.})}{[k_T(\infty)]_1} = \frac{\alpha(\text{exp.})}{[\alpha(\infty)]_1},$$

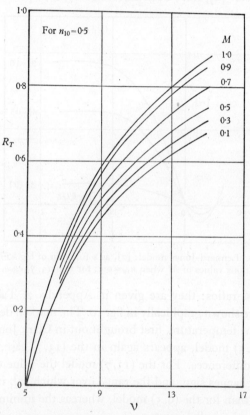

Fig. 11. Inverse power repulsion: the thermal separation ratio R_T as a function of the force index ν for various values of M and for $n_{10} = 0.5$.

where the quantities in the denominator refer to rigid spheres. R_T is thus a measure of the extent to which the interactions approach the ideally hard ones of rigid spheres. It is less dependent on the relative proportions of the components than is α, and it can therefore be regarded roughly as a characteristic of the mixture at a given temperature.

The corresponding theoretical quantity is

$$R_T \text{ (th.)} = \frac{k_T}{[k_T(\infty)]_1} = \frac{\alpha}{[\alpha(\infty)]_1},$$

where k_T and α are the values of the thermal diffusion ratio for an assumed law of force. R_T (th.) can be found readily only for isotopic mixtures; for non-isotopic mixtures it is necessary to know the relation between the collision integrals $\Omega_1, \Omega_2, \Omega_{12}$. In this expression for R_T (th.) the upper term is the exact value of k_T or α, not the first approximation. The distinction is important if R_T (th.) is to be compared with experimental values, for the error of the first approximation is considerably greater than the experimental error. Unfortunately, it is known exactly only in the special case of a Lorentzian gas, though an estimate has been made for other cases (Grew, 1941).

For an isotopic mixture in which the intermolecular force is an inverse power repulsion, $F = \kappa r^{-\nu}$, the relation between R_T (th.) and ν is shown in fig. 11. In calculating R_T (th.) allowance has been made for the error of the first approximation. These curves can be used in conjunction with experimental values of R_T to determine the force index of the interactions in the experimental mixture.

CHAPTER III

EXPERIMENTAL METHODS

3.1. Experimental determination of the thermal diffusion factor

Experimental investigations of thermal diffusion have usually been based on the determination of the difference in composition of two parts of a gas mixture which are at different temperatures. This is the principle of the first experiments of Chapman and Dootson (1917) to which reference has already been made.

In the usual procedure, a binary gas mixture of known composition is contained in a vessel consisting of two bulbs joined by a tube of relatively small section. A temperature gradient is set up in this tube by bringing the bulbs to different temperatures, uniform over each bulb. Thermal diffusion produces, as we have seen (§1.2), a concentration gradient which, when a steady state is attained, is related to the temperature gradient by

$$\frac{\partial n_{10}}{\partial \mathbf{r}} = -k_T \frac{1}{T} \frac{\partial T}{\partial \mathbf{r}},$$

where n_{10} is the relative proportion of the heavier molecule. Assuming the range of temperature and concentration is small so that k_T can be regarded as constant, the equation can be integrated to give the difference in composition in the two bulbs; thus

$$n_{10} - n'_{10} = k_T \ln(T'/T), \qquad (3.1)$$

where n_{10} and n'_{10} are the proportionate number densities of the heavier molecules in the bulbs at temperatures T and T' respectively. The difference $(n_{10} - n'_{10})$ is the separation S; it is this quantity which has usually been stated in the experimental results. The ratio $S/\ln(T'/T)$ gives a mean value of k_T in the range of temperature and concentration concerned.

An alternative procedure, theoretically preferable, since it does not involve the assumption that k_T is independent of concentration, is as follows. In terms of the thermal diffusion factor the equation of diffusion is

$$\frac{\partial n_{10}}{\partial \mathbf{r}} = -\alpha n_{10} n_{20} \frac{\partial(\ln T)}{\partial \mathbf{r}}.$$

To integrate we assume that α is independent of temperature and concentration; an assumption which, as regards the concentration, is much more justifiable than in the case of k_T. Then

$$\frac{dn_{10}}{n_{10}n_{20}} = \frac{dn_{10}}{n_{10}(1-n_{10})} = -\alpha d(\ln T)$$

and
$$\frac{n_{10}}{n_{20}} = AT^{-\alpha}, \quad \text{where } A \text{ is a constant.}$$

The ratio $\dfrac{n_{10}}{n_{20}}\bigg/\dfrac{n'_{10}}{n'_{20}}$ is called the separation factor q, hence $q = (T'/T)^\alpha$

and
$$\alpha = \ln q / \ln \frac{T'}{T}. \tag{3.2}$$

In much of the experimental work, however, it is the separation, not the separation factor, which has been found. Since the separation is strongly dependent on the composition, in considering a series of separation measurements relating to a particular mixture but made, for example, at different temperatures, account should be taken of the fact that usually each measurement refers to a different mean composition.

3.2. Measurement of the separation

In finding the separation it is not always convenient, nor is it necessary, to determine the composition of the mixture in both bulbs. The separation can be found from the change in composition which occurs in one bulb only, provided the ratio of the volumes of the two bulbs is known. For in the thermal diffusion process the number of heavier molecules transferred to one bulb is equal to the number of lighter molecules transferred to the other. The changes in composition which occur in each bulb are therefore in the inverse ratio of the numbers of molecules in each bulb, and thus depend on the volume and the temperature. If V is the volume of the bulb at temperature T, V' that of the bulb at temperature T', and s is the observed change in composition due to thermal diffusion in the bulb at temperature T, the change in the other bulb is easily shown to be $s(VT'/V'T)$, and the separation is therefore

$$S = s\left(1 + \frac{VT'}{V'T}\right) = s(1+f), \quad \text{where } f = VT'/V'T. \tag{3.3}$$

Thus the separation, or the separation factor, can be calculated from the change in composition which occurs in one bulb only. It is

clear from the expression for the separation that the bulb in which
the change in composition is measured should be the smaller. In
deducing the expression for the separation the volume of the
connecting tube has been neglected; a correction must be made if
this is not permissible.

Method of multiple separations. When the separation is very small,
as with most isotopic mixtures, a measurable change in composition
can be produced by repetition of the diffusion process. This
procedure requires a stopcock between the bulbs so that one of them
can be evacuated. The gas mixture is allowed to reach equilibrium
within the bulbs A and B at temperatures T and T' respectively.
B is then evacuated and the mixture in A, now enriched in one of
the components as compared with the original mixture, is admitted
to it. Thermal diffusion again occurs, and again when equilibrium
is reached B is evacuated and filled with gas from A. After several
repetitions the composition of the gas remaining in A is determined,
and the difference Δ between this and the initial composition
calculated. If the number of repetitions is n, then it can easily be
shown that $\Delta = ns$ and the separation $S = \Delta/n \cdot (1+f)$. Each separation occurs, of course, at a different pressure, but theory and
experiment agree in showing that, at least at pressures below 1 or
2 atm., the separation is independent of the pressure. The diminution of pressure does, however, limit the number of repetitions
which may be made; in the experiments of Nier (1939, 1940 a, b)
and Stier (1942) on the neon and argon isotopes this number did
not exceed 12.

The approach to the steady state. Clark Jones and Furry (1946)
have shown theoretically that the steady state is approached
exponentially, a result which is confirmed by some as yet unpublished experiments of Nettley. The theory shows that the time
required for the change in composition to reach to within $1/e$th of
the final steady value (i.e. the relaxation time) is proportional to the
length of the connecting tube and inversely proportional to its
cross-sectional area; the time varies directly as the pressure also.
For rapid attainment of the steady state it is advantageous to work
at low pressures and to use a diffusion vessel of which at least one
of the bulbs is small in volume. An account of the theory is given
in Appendix 3.

3.3. Methods of analysis

A number of methods have been used for measuring the change in composition resulting from thermal diffusion. This change, even in the most favourable cases, seldom exceeds 10 % and is usually much smaller; its precise determination is frequently difficult.

In some early investigations the gas was analysed by chemical methods, but for many mixtures there are more rapid and convenient methods depending on the variation with composition of properties such as thermal conductivity, viscosity and optical refractivity. Isotopic mixtures, to which alone the theory of thermal diffusion as so far developed is readily applicable, are unfortunately the most difficult to study experimentally—not only because of the difficulty of analysis, but also because the separation is small. The development in recent years of mass spectrometers adapted for the measurement of relative abundances, however, has enabled some progress to be made. Another analytical technique is applicable in the special case when one of the components is radioactive. An account of the application of these methods of analysis in thermal diffusion measurements follows.

From the variation of thermal conductivity. An instrument devised by Shakespear and called by him a 'katharometer' was applied by Ibbs (1921) in his first experiments on thermal diffusion. The katharometer, the use of which has been discussed by Daynes (1920), consists of two similar platinum spirals about 1 cm. in length, mounted axially in holes or 'cells' drilled in a copper block (cf. K, fig. 2). The spirals are of wire about 0·001 in. in diameter, the diameter of the spiral being 1 mm. The spirals form two arms of a Wheatstone bridge. The current through the bridge (about 100 mA.) raises the temperature of the spirals above that of the block, the excess temperature of each spiral being dependent on the thermal conductivity of the gas surrounding it. One of the spirals is permanently sealed in air or other gas; when the other is exposed to a gas of different conductivity, the temperatures of the spirals, and therefore the resistances, differ, and the bridge is thrown out of balance, assuming it is balanced when both spirals are surrounded by the same gas.

To find the relative proportions of the components of a gas mixture the instrument is first calibrated. This is done by admitting

mixtures of known proportions to the open cell and observing either
the deflexion of the galvanometer connected across the bridge, the
resistances of the other arms being constant, or the change in
resistance of one of these arms required to restore balance. The
precision with which a change in composition of a mixture can be
measured depends of course on the difference in the thermal conductivities of the two components, and this in turn depends on the
difference of the molecular masses. For a mixture such as hydrogen-
nitrogen in about equal proportions the percentage separation can
be determined to within about 0·02; for hydrogen-helium mixtures,
for which the mass ratio is small, the error is about 0·1. The
katharometer has the advantage that its open cell can form part of
the diffusion vessel, and so it can indicate continuously the changes
in composition as thermal diffusion proceeds. The arrangement
used by Ibbs and his collaborators is shown in fig. 2.

The *thermal conductivity microgauge*, developed by Bolland and
Melville (1937) for the analysis of small samples, is based on the
same principle as the katharometer. As used by Grew (1947) for the
investigation of thermal diffusion in inert gases, it consisted of
a tungsten spiral filament, of length about 2·5 cm. and diameter
0·2 mm., supported by platinum leads in a capillary tube of 2 mm.
bore. The capillary tube G was connected to a bulb A (fig. 12) and
mercury reservoir R, so that a sample of gas taken from the diffusion
vessel V, V', and admitted to the bulb A, could be compressed
around the filament to a prescribed amount—50 mm. of mercury
was adopted as a standard pressure. The filament, of which the
resistance was 20 ohms, formed one arm of a bridge. Two of the
other arms were manganin resistors both of 10 ohms resistance; the
remaining arm was a coil C of the same resistance as the filament
when this was at a temperature approximately 20° above that of its
surroundings. This coil was designed to have the same temperature
coefficient of resistance as that of the filament and so to compensate
the effect of any fluctuations in the temperature of the paraffin bath
in which the capillary tube, compression bulbs, and the three
resistors were all immersed. The temperature of the bath was 21° C.
The balance of the bridge could be maintained as the composition
of the gas about the filament varied either by change of resistance
of one of the arms, or more conveniently by varying the current

through the bridge to keep the filament temperature constant. The percentage composition of a hydrogen-helium mixture could be found to within about 0·07 and of a helium-argon mixture to within about 0·01.

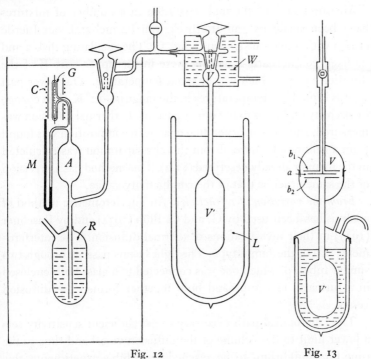

Fig. 12   Fig. 13

Fig. 12. Diffusion apparatus with thermal conductivity microgauge. V, V', diffusion bulbs; G, microgauge; W, water bath; L, refrigerant; M, manometer; C, resistance coil. (Grew, 1947.)

Fig. 13. Measurement of the separation from the change in viscosity. a, oscillating disk; b_1, b_2, fixed disks; V, V', the diffusion bulbs. After van Itterbeek, van Paemel and van Lierde (1947).

With this form of conductivity gauge the sample required for analysis may be so small that it can be abstracted from the diffusion vessel without appreciable disturbance of the conditions there. The size of the sample depends of course on the dead space between diffusion vessel and gauge; but 0·2 cm.³ at s.t.p. can be sufficient.

From the variation of viscosity. Investigating the dependence of the viscosity of a gas on temperature, van Itterbeek and van Paemel (1938, 1940) have developed the method of measurement based on the damping of an oscillating disk. The method is readily applied to the analysis of a gas mixture, the viscosity of which is of course dependent on the relative proportions of the components, and it can therefore be used in a study of thermal diffusion.

Measurements of thermal separation in a number of mixtures have been made by van Itterbeek, van Paemel and van Lierde (1947) with apparatus shown in fig. 13. The oscillating disk a and its fixed counterparts b_1 and b_2 were in the upper part V of the diffusion vessel, which was at room temperature. The lower part V' was brought to temperatures in the range 90–12° K. The change in viscosity of the gas in the upper part due to thermal diffusion was measured, and the corresponding change in composition was found from a calibration curve. From this the separation was calculated in the manner already described (§3.2). This method has a precision of the same order as that of the conductivity gauge.

From the variation of refractivity. An interferometric method of analysis has been used by G. and O. Blüh (1934) and by Puschner (1937) in their investigations of thermal diffusion. The interferometer was of the Jamin type. The light beams passed through two similar tubes, of which one was connected to a glass bulb enclosed in a furnace. This tube and bulb together formed the diffusion vessel.

The long optical path necessary to get sufficient sensitivity sets a lower limit to the volume of the diffusion vessel and thus to the time for equilibrium to be reached. In Blüh's experiments, this time, with mixtures containing hydrogen, was 40–60 min. The method is less convenient than that depending on conductivity changes but it has advantages in particular cases. The conductivity method is clearly inapplicable if the conductivities of the two components of a gas mixture are nearly the same; the refractivities of these same gases may, however, be widely different.

Analysis by mass spectrometer. For the study of thermal diffusion in isotopic mixtures, with the exception of hydrogen-deuterium, a mass spectrometer is necessary. In recent years Nier (1940c) and others have developed instruments for the measurement of relative abundance which are simpler than those of high-resolving power required for the precise determination of mass. In the Nier type of mass spectrometer the mixture is first ionized by passage through an electron beam; the ions so formed are accelerated by an electric field and then passed through a slit system into a magnetic field by which they are deflected through an angle which depends on the mass and velocity. By variation of either the magnetic field or the electric field ions of different masses can be brought in turn on to a collecting electrode; the corresponding ion currents are measured after amplification, and these are a measure of the relative numbers of ions in the different mass ranges. The magnetic field is usually of sector form, of angle $\frac{1}{3}\pi$ or $\frac{1}{2}\pi$ radians. The axis of the ion beam is normal to the field both where it enters and where it leaves—in these conditions the beam is focused at a point on the line joining the entrance slit and the centre of curvature of the path; this permits the use of fairly wide slits with consequent increase in intensity. The relative abundance of, for example, the isotopes of neon can be determined in this way to about 0·1 %. The error in determining the thermal separation in an isotopic mixture is usually about 5–10 %.

Analysis by radioactivity. Another means of analysis is applicable when one of the components is radioactive. In this case, since radioactive estimation is very sensitive, the radioactive component need be present in only minute concentration. A simplification then results in the theory. A study of thermal diffusion in mixtures containing radon has been made by Harrison (1937, 1942).

In Harrison's experiments the diffusion vessel, V, V', consisted of a uniform tube of glass, 30 cm. long and 1 cm. bore, which was divided into two approximately equal parts by a stopcock S_1 (fig. 14). The two parts were connected also by a capillary tube P provided with a cock S_2. One part was immersed in an ice-bath, the other was surrounded by an electric heater. The vessel was mounted in front of a lead block in which were two apertures A, B, placed to transmit γ-radiation from the middle region of each part. The width of the aperture B was variable. Opposite these apertures were two ionization chambers, I_1, I_2, charged and connected in such a way as to measure the difference in the flux of γ-radiation through the apertures. A uniform mixture of, for example, radon and helium was introduced into the vessel and the two parts brought to 100 and 0° C., the pressure being equalized by opening the cock S_2, S_1 remaining closed. Time was then allowed for radioactive equilibrium to be established; thereafter the flux of γ-radiation (which originates in the disintegration of the decay products Ra A and Ra B) is a measure of the amount of radon. The quantities of radiation entering the two ionization chambers were then made equal by adjustment of the width of the aperture B until

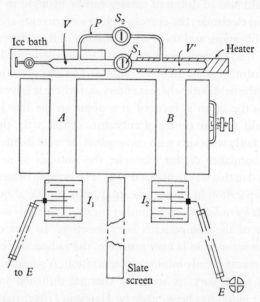

Fig. 14. Measurement of separation in a radioactive mixture. V, V', the diffusion bulbs; P, capillary connecting tube; A, B, apertures in lead blocks; I_1, I_2, ionization chambers; E, electrometer. (Harrison, 1937.)

the ionization current was zero. The large-bore cock S_1 was opened for a time sufficient for thermal diffusion to occur and for the gas to reach an equilibrium state. There was then a resultant ionization current, since the amounts of radon opposite the two apertures were no longer equal. The difference of these amounts was determined from the current and a calibration curve obtained with the use of standard radium needles.

CHAPTER IV

EXPERIMENTAL RESULTS

Some early experimental results have already been given (Chapter I). Of later work the most important for its bearing on the theory is that on mixtures of the inert gases, especially isotopic mixtures, for here the molecules are spherical, non-polar and monatomic and therefore approach most nearly the type of molecule postulated in the theory. The results for these mixtures form therefore the major part of the following account. A list of all mixtures which have been examined, with a summary of results, is given in Appendix 6.

To compare the results of thermal diffusion measurements with those of related phenomena such as viscosity, it is convenient to assume that the molecules interact as centres of inverse power repulsion. This model has the advantage of simplicity and it was until recently the only one for which theoretical values of the collision integrals were available. We have seen how for this model the thermal diffusion factor α and the separation ratio R_T can be calculated, and curves have been given of R_T as a function of the force index ν for various values of the proportionate mass difference M. A comparison of the experimental values of R_T with these theoretical values then enables the force index of the actual molecular encounters to be determined. As viscosity measurements also lead to a value of the force index we have here a means of examining the consistency of thermal diffusion and viscosity measurements. This procedure is strictly applicable only to isotopic mixtures. For non-isotopic mixtures the existence of three types of interaction is a complication and theoretical values of R_T cannot usefully be calculated. We may, however, compare experimental values of R_T for non-isotopic mixtures with the theoretical values for isotopic mixtures of the same mass ratio, and thus determine a force index for the mixture. The exact significance of the index, which is denoted by $\bar{\nu}$, cannot be stated, but it approximates to ν_{12}, the index appropriate to interactions of unlike molecules; this is evident from the form of the expression for α which shows that R_T is little affected by the values of ν_1 and ν_2. Values of the force index found in this way are given in the following survey of experimental results.

The results are given in the following order:

(i) Non-isotopic mixtures of the inert gases.

(ii) Isotopic mixtures: neon, argon, helium, hydrogen, oxygen, nitrogen, methane and ammonia.

(iii) Some other mixtures, including hydrogen with helium, nitrogen and carbon dioxide.

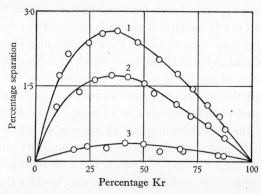

Fig. 15. Separation as a function of composition for mixtures of krypton with (1) helium, (2) neon, (3) argon; $T = 15°$ C., $T' = 100°$ C. After Atkins, Bastick and Ibbs (1939).

4.1. The inert gas mixtures: non-isotopic

The separation as a function of composition. All the binary combinations of the inert gases, except those containing radon, were examined by Atkins, Bastick and Ibbs (1939), who determined the separation as a function of composition for constant temperatures of the two parts of the diffusion vessel. These temperatures were $T = 288°$ K. and $T' = 373°$ K. The katharometer method of analysis was used with apparatus similar to that shown in fig. 2.

Some typical curves are shown in fig. 15. The asymmetry of the curves shows that the thermal diffusion factor α varies appreciably with the composition; in all these mixtures it decreases progressively as the proportion of the heavier component increases. This is in conformity with the theory. The variation is shown graphically in fig. 16. A further reference to this point is made later (§ 5.1).

For a given mixture, the thermal separation ratio R_T exhibits a relatively small variation with composition; usually it decreases with increasing content of the heavier component (cf. fig. 16). In passing from one mixture to another there is a progressive decrease as a heavier molecule is substituted for a lighter. This change is brought out in Table I where, above the diagonal line, the mean values of R_T for the various mixtures are summarized. The numbers below the line are values of the force index $\bar{\nu}$ found by interpolation

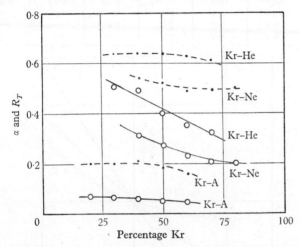

Fig. 16. Variation with composition of the thermal diffusion factor α, and separation ratio R_T for mixtures of krypton with helium, neon and argon. —○— α; —●—●— R_T.

from the theoretical curves of R_T as a function of ν for isotopic mixtures of various mass differences. (These values differ from those already published, which were based on theoretical values of R_T appropriate to a Lorentzian gas.) The table includes also the results for mixtures containing radon which are due to Harrison (1937, 1942); it is interesting that, despite the special conditions in which they were obtained, these values fall properly into place in the scheme.

In this particular temperature interval, therefore, the inert gases exhibit a wide range of behaviour, diminishing in hardness with increasing mass. Subsequent work, however, shows that R_T is dependent on the temperature, and that this difference in behaviour is no longer apparent if the various mixtures are compared at 'corresponding' temperatures related to the critical temperatures of the components (§5.4).

TABLE I. *Values of the ratio R_T and the force index $\tilde{v}$ for inert gas mixtures. R_T above diagonal line, $\tilde{v}$ below*

	He	Ne	A	Kr	Xe	Rn
He		0·80	0·65	0·63	0·59	0·23
Ne	15·3		0·54	0·51	0·43	0·12
A	10·6	10·2		0·19	0·17	0·02
Kr	9·8	9·0	6·0		0·08	—
Xe	9·2	7·8	5·8	5·4		—
Rn	6·4	6·1	5·1	—	—	

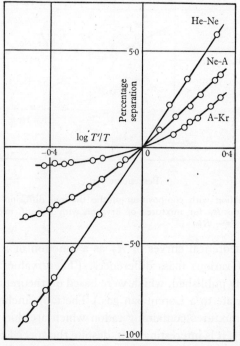

Fig. 17. Relation between separation and log T'/T for helium-neon (53·8 % He), neon-argon (51·2 % Ne) and argon-krypton (53·5 % A) mixtures. $T = 293°$ K. throughout. (Grew, 1947.)

The separation as a function of temperature. The same mixtures were examined over an extended range of temperature by Grew (1947), with the apparatus shown in fig. 12. A thermal conductivity microgauge was used for analysis. The diffusion vessel V, V' could be rotated about a horizontal axis. The volumes of the two parts were $V = 2·6$ cm.³ and $V' = 61$ cm.³ For measurements at low temperatures the larger bulb was brought below the smaller and immersed in a refrigerant; for higher temperatures the position was reversed, the larger bulb being now the upper and enclosed in an electric heater. The temperature of the smaller bulb was constant at a value $T = 20°$ C. The change in composition in this bulb due to thermal diffusion was measured for different values of the temperature T' of the larger bulb, and the separation calculated from this in the usual way. Some results are shown graphically in fig. 17.

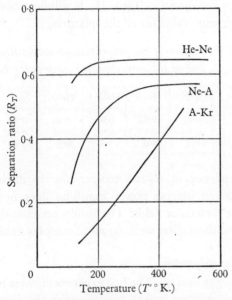

Fig. 18. The separation ratio R_T at various temperatures for helium-neon, neon-argon and argon-krypton mixtures.

It appears that, in general, although the separation S is approximately proportional to $\ln(T'/T)$ at the higher values of T', at the other extreme it is noticeably less (numerically) than that expected if the proportionality continued to hold. α is therefore dependent on the temperature. Its value at any temperature can be found from the slope of the $S \sim \ln(T'/T)$ curves, for

$$S = \int_T^{T'} \alpha n_{10} n_{20} \, d(\ln T),$$

and in the experimental method T is constant, so that the value of α at temperature T' is $n_{10} n_{20} \, dS/d(\ln T')$. The values of R_T shown in fig. 18 and Appendix 5 are calculated as the ratio of α (exp.), thus determined, and $[\alpha(\infty)]_1$, the theoretical value for molecules of the same size and mass interacting as rigid spheres. The error is estimated as 1–2 %.

The results show that generally R_T increases with increasing temperature, the rate of change diminishing, however, until in most cases R_T becomes sensibly constant. The maximum value of R_T and of the corresponding force index $\tilde{\nu}_{(max.)}$ deduced in the way described above are shown in Table II. It will be noticed that $\tilde{\nu}_{(max.)}$ has much the same value for all the mixtures.

TABLE II. *Values of the proportionate mass ratio M, of $R_{T(max.)}$ and of the corresponding force index $\tilde{\nu}_{(max.)}$*

Mixture	He-Ne	He-A	He-Kr	He-X	Ne-A	Ne-Kr
M	0·67	0·82	0·91	0·94	0·33	0·61
$R_{T(max.)}$	0·64	0·66	0·67	0·66	0·57	0·64
$\tilde{\nu}_{(max.)}$	11·0	10·9	10·8	10·5	10·9	11·2

The dependence of R_T on temperature in its lower ranges indicates that an inverse power repulsion does not adequately represent the molecular fields. The results are considered later in relation to the theoretical work on more complex fields.

4.2. Isotopic mixtures

Neon and argon isotopes. The first experiments were made by Nier (1939, 1940 a, b); Stier (1942), working with the same apparatus, has repeated the measurements over an extended temperature range. Because of the extremely small value of the thermal diffusion factor in these mixtures, a result of the small mass difference, the method of multiple separations was applied (§ 3.2) and large temperature differences were used, the temperature T, T' of both bulbs varying in the series of measurements.

The diffusion vessel consisted of two bulbs, each of 100 cm.³ capacity, connected by a tube 7 cm. long and 8·5 mm. diameter (internal) provided with a stopcock. In Stier's experiments the temperature of the connecting tube and cock was controlled by circulating water. The bulbs were brought to different temperatures by surrounding them with a refrigerant or electrically heated oven.

The mixtures were analysed by means of a mass spectrometer. The proportions of the isotopes in the gas before diffusion were those naturally occurring, that is, the neon contained $9\cdot93\%$ ^{22}Ne, and the argon $0\cdot307\%$ ^{36}A.

From the measured separation with the bulbs at temperatures T and T' the mean value $\bar{\alpha}$ of the thermal diffusion factor in the range $T \to T'$ was calculated. An argument given by Harrison Brown (1940) shows that the mean value thus found can be identified with the actual value of α at a temperature T_r within the range $T \to T'$ given by

$$T_r = \frac{TT'}{T'-T} \ln \frac{T'}{T}.$$

The argument, which is reproduced in Appendix 4, assumes that α varies with temperature according to the relation

$$\alpha = \alpha_0 (1 - A/T),$$

where A is a constant and α_0 is the limiting value of α at high temperatures.

Stier's results are shown in fig. 19. As in the case of non-isotopic mixtures, α and R_T decrease with decreasing temperature. Here, however, there appears to be a linear relation between R_T and $\ln T_r$; the experimental observations lie close to the curves

$$R_T = 0\cdot25 \ln \frac{T_r}{26\cdot6}, \quad \text{for neon,}$$

and

$$R_T = 0\cdot25 \ln \frac{T_r}{86\cdot9}, \quad \text{for argon.}$$

The persistent increase in R_T which appears in neon at the higher temperatures is unexpected from the behaviour of non-isotopic mixtures containing neon as one component. For example, neon-helium and neon-argon both give nearly constant values of R_T at these same temperatures. It is desirable that further experiments should be made.

Helium isotopes. Nier in collaboration with McInteer and Aldrich (1947) has used the same apparatus for separation measurements with the isotopic mixture ^{3}He-^{4}He. The abundance of ^{3}He was first increased by means of a separating column to about 300 times its normal value of $1\cdot6 \times 10^{-7}$. Separation measurements were then made with the bulbs at temperatures $T = 273°$ K. and $T' = 613°$ K.

The value of the thermal diffusion factor thus determined was 0.059 ± 0.005. The value for molecules which behave as rigid elastic spheres is $[\alpha(\infty)]_1 = 0.121$; the value of R_T is therefore 0.49, which corresponds with a repulsive force index $\nu = 9.5$. These values are much smaller than would be expected from other properties such as the viscosity, and it seems probable that the error in these difficult measurements is greater than that estimated.

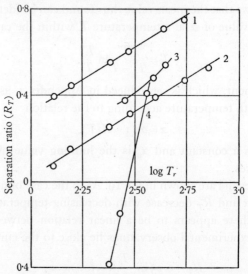

Fig. 19. The variation of the separation ratio R_T with temperature for isotopic mixtures. (1) ^{20}Ne-^{22}Ne, (2) ^{36}A-^{40}A, (3) $^{16}O^{16}O$-$^{16}O^{18}O$, (4) $^{14}NH_3$-$^{15}NH_3$. (From Stier, 1942; Whalley, Winter and Briscoe, 1949; and Watson and Woernley, 1943.)

Hydrogen-deuterium. The comparatively large mass ratio of the hydrogen isotopes allows the use of analytical methods based on the variation of viscosity or thermal conductivity with composition. Heath, Ibbs and Wild (1941) used the katharometer to measure the separation in mixtures of widely varying composition, the temperature range being 15–100° C. Their results are shown graphically in fig. 31, where the slight dependence of α on composition is noticeable. Hydrogen-deuterium is still the only isotopic mixture which has been examined over a range of composition.

The temperature dependence of the thermal diffusion factor has been investigated by Grew (1941) and by de Troyer, van Itterbeek and Rietveld (1951). Grew used the method later applied to the inert gases (cf. §3.3). He concluded that between 700 and 90° K. the factor is independent of temperature, and subsequent more precise experiments confirm this. De Troyer, van Itterbeek and Rietveld have made measurements at extremely low temperatures, determining the separation from the variation of viscosity. The temperature T of one bulb was constant at 293° K. while the temperature T' of the other was in the range 90–16° K. Their results show that, as T' falls below 90° K., the numerical value of the separation S falls increasingly below the value expected if the proportionality between S and $\ln T'/T$ existing at higher temperatures were preserved; it attains a maximum value at about $T' = 25°$ K. and then decreases—the observed separation with $T' = 16$ being less than that with $T' = 20°$ K. The thermal diffusion factor thus decreases with decreasing temperature at first in much the same way as in the inert gas and other mixtures; here, however, the decrease continues beyond what has hitherto been observed, so that α first becomes zero and then assumes negative values. This reversal of sign is, of course, of much theoretical importance.

TABLE III. *The thermal diffusion factor α, and thermal separation ratio R_T, for a hydrogen-deuterium mixture of equal proportions (from measurements of de Troyer, van Itterbeek and Rietveld, 1951)*

Temp. °K.	293–90	80	60	40	30	20
α	0·190	0·167	0·119	0·061	0·021	−0·028
R_T	0·69	0·61	0·43	0·22	0·08	−0·102
R_T (13, 7)	0·62→0·45	0·38	0·24	0·10	0·02	−0·06

The variation of α with temperature is shown in Table III. The values of α are deduced from the separation factor $\sim \ln T'/T$ curves derived from the measurements of de Troyer, van Itterbeek and Rietveld; as there are only four experimental points for the range $T' = 90 \to 16°$ K., the values are subject to considerable error, but they suffice to indicate the trend of α with temperature. The table includes values of R_T calculated for this mixture assuming the molecules interact according to the Lennard-Jones (13, 7) force law; these are referred to later.

Isotopic oxygen, nitrogen and methane. An investigation of thermal diffusion in the mixture $^{16}O^{16}O$-$^{16}O^{18}O$ has been made by

Whalley, Winter and Briscoe (1949); and Davenport and Winter (1951) have examined the mixtures $^{14}N^{14}N$-$^{14}N^{15}N$, $^{12}C^{16}O$-$^{13}C^{16}O$, and $^{12}CH_4$-$^{13}CH_4$. The method in both cases was essentially the same as that of Stier, though here the proportion of the rarer isotope was sometimes increased above the normal value by means of a separating column. The volumes of the diffusion bulbs were 1085 and 940 cm.³ respectively; the connecting tube was 2 cm. in diameter and 22 cm. long, and a correction was made for the change in composition which occurs there. Some results are shown in Table IV. The last column contains theoretical values of R_T calculated for the Lennard-Jones (13, 7) model.

TABLE IV. *Values of the thermal diffusion factor α, and thermal separation ratio R_T, for some isotopic mixtures (from Whalley, Winter and Briscoe, 1949, and Davenport and Winter, 1951)*

Mixture	$T°$K.	$T'°$K.	$T_r°$K.	$10^3 \alpha$	R_T	R_T (13, 7)
$^{16}O^{16}O$-$^{16}O^{18}O$	195	373	264	9·9 ± 0·8	0·37	0·35
	295	528	389	12·8 ± 0·6	0·48	0·50
	296	703	443	14·5 ± 0·6	0·54	0·50
$^{14}N^{14}N$-$^{14}N^{15}N$	195	429	286	7·1 ± 0·5	0·47	0·44
	294	678	434	9·1 ± 0·4	0·58	0·54
$^{12}CH_4$-$^{13}CH_4$	195	433	289	7·2 ± 0·7	0·27	0·30
	295	708	448	11 ± 1	0·41	0·45

Isotopic ammonia. Watson and Woernley (1943) investigated the mixture $^{14}NH_3$-$^{15}NH_3$, in the expectation that, because of the small repulsive force index (indicated by viscosity measurements) and strong attractive field of the ammonia molecule, the reversal of sign of α associated with molecules of the Lennard-Jones type might here occur. Their results, which are given in fig. 19, show clearly that such a reversal of sign does indeed occur at a temperature near to 293° K. This was the first time that this effect had been observed, though, as stated above, it has since been found in hydrogen-deuterium mixtures.

4.3. Some other mixtures

Hydrogen-helium. Viscosity measurements indicate that in this mixture the heavier molecule is the smaller in diameter; for helium

$\sigma_1 = 2\cdot 18$ A., for hydrogen $\sigma_2 = 2\cdot 74$ A. The effects of the mass difference and of the size difference are thus opposed; the former, however, is dominant.

The first measurements were made by Elliott and Masson (1925), who used a diffusion vessel consisting of two bulbs of 22 and 32 cm.³ capacity at temperatures of 0 and 490° C. respectively. Their results, which cover a range of composition from 30 to 60 % hydrogen, lead to a mean value of R_T of 0·60.

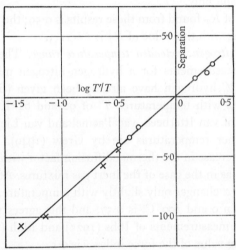

Fig. 20. The relation between separation and log T'/T for a hydrogen-helium mixture (53·6 % H_2). $T = 293°$ K. throughout. × Van Itterbeek, van Paemel and van Lierde (1947); ○ Grew (1947).

Van Itterbeek, van Paemel and van Lierde (1947) have made measurements at extremely low temperatures using the variation of viscosity to determine the composition. The temperature T of one bulb of their diffusion vessel was constant at 292° K., while the temperature T' of the other was in the range 12–90° K. These mixtures have been examined also by Grew (1949) with the apparatus used for the inert gas mixtures. The measurements cover the range $T' = 90 \rightarrow 600°$ K. with $T = 293°$ K. Fig. 20 shows the separation as a function of log (T'/T) for a mixture containing 53·6 % hydrogen; the values at the lowest temperatures T' have been found by interpolation in the results of van Itterbeek, van Paemel and van Lierde.

It appears that a linear relation between separation and log T'/T holds over the temperature range from $T' = 600°$ K. to $20°$ K. (where log $T'/T = -1.15$). More recent work by de Troyer, van Itterbeek and Rietveld (1951) confirms the linearity in the range $293-20°$ K., but at still lower temperatures there is evidence of a departure from the linear relation. Above $20°$ K. therefore the thermal diffusion factor is independent of temperature, and this implies that the interactions can here be represented by an inverse power repulsion only.

The value of R_T found from these results is 0.59; the force index corresponding with this value of R_T is $\tilde{\nu} = 11.3$.

Hydrogen-nitrogen: extended temperature range. The results of separation measurements for a hydrogen-nitrogen mixture containing 39.8% hydrogen have already been given (fig. 5). The measurements with temperatures T' of 90 and $64°$ K. are taken from results of van Itterbeek, van Paemel and van Lierde (1947); those at higher temperatures are by Grew (1949). The curve indicates a decrease in the thermal diffusion factor with decreasing temperature, as in the case of the inert gas mixtures. At the higher temperatures α changes only slightly with temperature. The value of R_T between 0 and $100°$ C. is 0.57, and this agrees with values derived from measurements of Ibbs (1925) and Blüh (1934). The corresponding value of the force index $\tilde{\nu}$ is 9.1.

Hydrogen-carbon dioxide. In this mixture the variation of α with temperature is apparent at relatively high temperatures. Lugg (1929) made separation measurements with the temperature T' extending to $470°$ C., T being $29°$ C. His results indicate that α increases with temperature in this range. Blüh (1934) obtained the results shown in fig. 21, using an interferometric method of analysis. This figure includes also results obtained by Grew. It is clear that there is an increase of α as the temperature increases, the increase being especially marked in the neighbourhood of $140°$ C. These results do not suggest, however, that α is discontinuous at this temperature, as Ibbs and Wakeman at one time proposed. The investigations over the extended temperature range show that the change is continuous.

Hydrogen, deuterium and helium with neon. De Troyer, van Itterbeek and van den Berg (1950) have made separation measurements for these mixtures at temperatures extending from 90 to 20° K. Their method of analysis from the viscosity variation is clearly applicable over a range of pressure, and in these experiments the pressure of the mixture could therefore be made so low that the neon did not condense above 20° K.

The decrease of the thermal diffusion factor with decreasing temperature, already known to occur at temperatures above 90° K.,

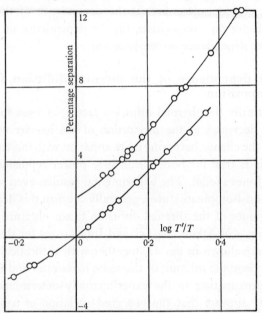

Fig. 21. The relation between separation and $\log T'/T$ for hydrogen-carbon dioxide mixtures. $T \sim 293°$ K. in both cases. Upper curve: Blüh, G. and O. (1934); lower curve, Grew (unpublished). To avoid overlapping, the upper curve has been displaced along the separation axis by 2 %.

becomes more pronounced as the temperature falls further. The change for helium-neon is, however, much smaller than for deuterium-neon and hydrogen-neon.

A summary of results for the numerous mixtures which have been examined is given in Appendix 6. It will be seen from this that the agreement of the measurements of different workers is not always satisfactory. Discrepancies among the values of the thermal diffusion factor are often as large as 5–10 %, though the relative accuracy of observations made by the same observer is certainly greater.

CHAPTER V

COMPARISON OF EXPERIMENTAL AND THEORETICAL RESULTS

In relating the experimental results with the theory the more important considerations are (i) the dependence of the thermal diffusion factor on composition, (ii) the dependence on pressure, and (iii) the dependence on temperature.

5.1. The dependence of the thermal diffusion factor on composition

Theoretically the thermal diffusion factor, at least for isotopic mixtures, decreases as the proportion of the heavier component increases, the change becoming more apparent with increasing mass ratio. This is true for both the inverse power repulsion and the Lennard-Jones model. The experimental results, even when they relate to non-isotopic mixtures, generally confirm this dependence.

Some values of the thermal diffusion factor obtained from the measurements of Atkins, Bastick and Ibbs (1939) for the inert gas mixtures are shown in fig. 22, together with theoretical values of $[\alpha]_1$ for an isotopic mixture of the same mass ratio and for a force index approximating to the experimentally determined index $\tilde{\nu}$ (p. 45). It appears that the observed variation of α with composition, although in the same sense as the theoretical variation, is in magnitude considerably greater. This conclusion is supported by the results of Waldman, obtained by means of the diffusion thermo-effect (cf. Chapter VI). For mixtures in which one component is rare Waldmann's method is more accurate than that depending on the measurement of the separation, and the results form a valuable contribution to the study of this aspect of thermal diffusion. Waldmann's experimental curves for hydrogen-nitrogen mixtures and for hydrogen-deuterium mixtures are shown in fig. 31.

A further correlation of theory and experiment in the general, non-isotopic case is difficult because of the complex dependence of the theoretical values of α on the relative proportions. Chapman (1940 b) has given a detailed discussion for the special case of the inverse power model. Of this we can refer to only one interesting point: it appears that in some mixtures in which the mass ratio is small there is the possibility that α may undergo a reversal of sign as the composition changes. That such a change of sign can occur has been shown experimentally.

Reversal of the sign of the thermal diffusion factor with changing composition. The general expression (2.12) for the thermal diffusion

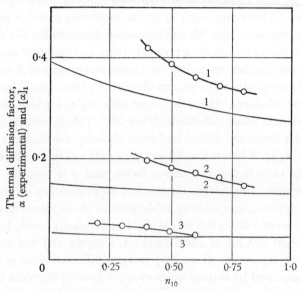

Fig. 22. The variation of the thermal diffusion factor with composition for (1) He-Ne, (2) Ne-A, (3) A-Kr. –O– experimental values (Atkins, Bastick and Ibbs, 1939); — theoretical values for centres of repulsion. (1) He-Ne, $M = 0.67$, $\nu = 15$; (2) Ne-A, $M = 0.33$, $\nu = 10$; (3) A-Kr, $M = 0.36$, $\nu = 6$.

factor is a product of two factors; the first, $5(C-1)$, depends only on the collision integrals relating to interaction of unlike molecules, the second is a function of the composition of the mixture and the quantities S and Q. The sign of this second factor, and therefore of α, depends on the signs and relative magnitudes of the products $S_1 n_{10}$ and $S_2 n_{20}$. Generally, as we have stated already, when the mass difference is large S_1 is positive and S_2 is negative, so that α is positive for all compositions, assuming, as we do henceforth, that $(C-1)$ is positive. This means that the heavier molecule diffuses down the temperature gradient. When, however, the mass difference is small, the signs of S_1 and S_2 are determined by the relative 'sizes', more precisely the relative extensions of the force fields, of the two molecular species. Usually the heavier molecule is the larger, and in this case again α is positive at all compositions. If, however, the heavier molecule is the smaller, S_1 may be negative and S_2 positive, leading to negative values of α at all compositions. This means that the heavier molecule diffuses up the temperature gradient. Or S_1 and S_2 may be of the same sign; this happens when the mean distance of closest approach of unlike molecules is either greater than, or less than, both the corresponding distances for like molecules. In this case, α shows a reversal of sign and therefore vanishes at a composition determined by the relative magnitudes of S_1 and S_2.

Such a reversal of sign has been observed by Grew (1944) in neon-ammonia mixtures. Here the mass ratio $m_1/m_2 = 1\cdot186$ and the proportionate mass difference $M = 0\cdot085$. Taking values of the molecular diameters determined from viscosity, the diameter ratio $\sigma_1/\sigma_2 = 0\cdot587$. When the molecules are treated as rigid spheres the diameter ratio is the dominating factor, and α is negative at all compositions. In studying the mixture experimentally no attempt was made to measure directly, in the manner already described, the thermal separation, as this was likely to be extremely small. Instead the method of Clusius and Dickel (cf. Chapter VII) was used in which the separation effected by thermal diffusion alone is many times increased by setting up convective counter-currents in the mixture.

The column used for the study of neon-ammonia and other mixtures consisted of two co-axial Pyrex tubes enclosed in a brass tube forming a water-jacket. The length of the column was 140 cm.; the external diameter of the inner tube was 18·2 mm., and the internal diameter of the outer tube was 30 mm. The outer tube was cooled by a flow of water at room temperature, and the inner one was heated to about 184° C. by aniline vapour. Samples of gas could be withdrawn from the upper and lower ends of the column and analysed by chemical means. Thus the difference in composition at the two ends when equilibrium had been attained was determined for a series of mixtures of varying proportions.

The results are shown in fig. 23, where the quantity termed the separation is the difference in the proportions of neon at the bottom and at the top of the column. It appears that from $0 \to 75\%$ Ne, the neon molecules concentrate at the top of the column; this implies diffusion of the neon molecules up the temperature gradient, and therefore a negative value of α in this range. From $75 \to 100\%$ Ne the reverse holds. Thus there is a reversal of sign of α at 75% Ne.

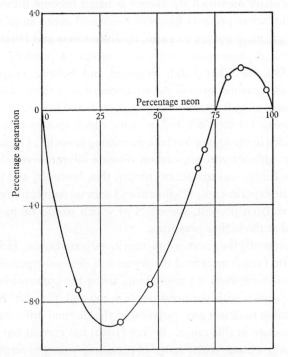

Fig. 23. The separation, produced in a Clusius-Dickel column, in neon-ammonia mixtures of various proportions.

No such reversal was observed in argon-hydrogen chloride, for which the mass ratio is smaller $(m_1/m_2 = 1\cdot095)$ but the diameter ratio is larger $(\sigma_1/\sigma_2 = 0\cdot815)$.

As Clusius (1949) has pointed out, this experiment is not altogether conclusive, as the neon used contained the isotope ^{22}Ne in the normal proportion of 10%, and the presence of this may have been important. A repetition of the experiment with the separated isotopes is desirable.

Leaf and Wall (1942) have used a column to show that α is negative for all proportions in carbon dioxide-cyclopropane mixtures.

5.2. Effect of pressure on thermal separation

It is convenient to refer here to the question of the effect of pressure on the thermal separation. Theoretically the separation is independent of pressure provided that this is not so extreme that the postulates on which the theory is based become invalid. This independence of pressure has been confirmed over a small range of pressure from about 0·3 to 1 atm. by Ibbs, Grew and Hirst (1929), who made experiments directly to investigate a possible pressure effect. On the other hand, Schmahl and Schewe (1940) have published measurements of the separation due to thermal diffusion in mixtures of hydrogen with carbon dioxide and hydrogen sulphide at pressures between 0·2 and 3·5 atm. which show a pronounced diminution in the separation with increasing pressure. Grew (1942), working with a hydrogen-carbon dioxide mixture over the same pressure range, was unable to confirm this, however, and it seems that in the experiments of Schmahl and Schewe convection currents may have been present, the effect of which would be more pronounced at the higher pressures.

More recently the question has been investigated again. Drickamer and Hofto (1949) measured the separation in neon-argon mixtures at pressures between 0·5 and 2 atm., using the conventional two-bulb apparatus with temperatures $T = 290$ and $T' = 480°$ K. They were unable to detect any variation of the thermal diffusion factor with pressure in this range. Becker (1950) has carried out experiments over a much wider range of pressure, from 3 to 80 atm. His apparatus consisted of two steel cylinders, each of 140 cm.³ capacity, connected by a steel tube. The lower one was maintained at about 14° C. and the upper at about 160° C. The bulbs were filled with gas mixtures prepared under pressure, and after allowing time for a steady state to be attained—several days at the higher pressures— the gas in each bulb was analysed chemically or by a thermal conductivity method.

The mixtures examined were nitrogen with hydrogen and methane, and carbon dioxide with hydrogen, nitrogen, argon and methane. In all cases, with the exception of nitrogen-methane, it was found that the thermal diffusion factor increased with increasing pressure. For a hydrogen-carbon dioxide mixture of equal proportions the increase in the range 3–80 atm. was threefold, for carbon dioxide-nitrogen eightfold. Nitrogen-hydrogen showed an increase of only 30 %, and in nitrogen-methane the thermal diffusion factor decreased with increasing pressure. The temperature dependence and the concentration dependence of the thermal diffusion factor also were found to be affected by pressure.

Becker has explained these results as a consequence of the imperfection of the gases. A simple argument leads to the conclusion that, when the behaviour of the components of a gas mixture departs from the ideal postulated in the theory, the separation obtained in a thermal diffusion apparatus contains, in addition to the contribution due to thermal diffusion, a second part due to the imperfect nature of the gases. Becker considers a hypothetical mixture in which only like molecules interact, so that thermal diffusion (which depends essentially on interactions of unlike molecules) cannot occur. The first component (1) is supposed to be ideal, the other (2) to conform with the simple equation of state

$$(p_2 + a/V_2^2)V_2 = RT,$$

where V_2 is the molar volume. When a temperature gradient is established in the mixture each component must distribute itself in such a way that its contribution to the total pressure is everywhere the same. For the ideal component then

$$p_1 = n_1 kT = n_1' kT',$$

where as usual n_1, n_1' refer to the number densities at temperatures T and T' respectively. For the real component

$$p_2 = \frac{RT}{V_2} - \frac{a}{V_2^2} = \frac{RT'}{V_2'} - \frac{a}{V_2'^2},$$

or since $V_2 = N_0/n_2$ (N_0 = Avogadro's number)

$$n_2 T - \frac{an_2^2}{N_0 R} = n_2' T' - \frac{an_2'^2}{N_0 R}.$$

From these equations it is clear that

$$\frac{n_1}{n_2} \neq \frac{n_1'}{n_2'}.$$

Thus there is a difference in composition of the mixture in the regions at temperatures T and T' resulting from the imperfection of one of the components, irrespective of the thermal diffusion process. Becker has estimated the magnitude of this contribution to the observed separation for hydrogen-carbon dioxide mixtures and shown that the apparent dependence of the thermal diffusion factor on pressure can thus be satisfactorily explained.

5.3. The dependence of the thermal diffusion factor on temperature

The experimental results show clearly that the thermal diffusion factor is a function of temperature. Although in detail the mode of dependence appears to be different in isotopic and non-isotopic mixtures, in both it is apparent that the thermal diffusion factor decreases as the temperature decreases. The simple inverse power model is therefore inadequate, for this model requires α to be independent of temperature,* and a more complex model, such as that of Lennard-Jones (§2.5), must be invoked if the experimental results are to be explained.

Before discussing the experimental results in relation to the Lennard-Jones model, however, it is convenient to consider them in terms of the inverse power model. Whether or not the molecular interactions in the experimental mixtures accord with an inverse power repulsion, we can use the relations between the thermal diffusion factor and force index which hold for this case to find from the experimental value of the thermal diffusion factor at a given temperature an effective force index at this temperature. The method of so doing has already been explained, and some values have been given with the experimental results. It is clear from the manner in which the thermal diffusion factor varies with the force index, illustrated in fig. 11, that the observed variation of the thermal diffusion factor implies a decrease in the effective force index as the temperature decreases. In other words, the molecules are softer the lower the temperature. If then the intermolecular

---

* It is true that for non-isotopic mixtures the quantities E_1 and E_2 (§2.6) for this model are temperature-dependent to an extent determined by the difference between the force indices for interactions of like and of unlike molecules. But an estimate, using likely values of these indices, suggests that the variation of α on this account would be quite insufficient to explain the observed variation (Cf. Chapman, 1940 b).

force is given, as we are supposing, by $F = \kappa r^{-\nu}$, ν must be regarded as a function of r, decreasing as r increases. The effective value of ν at low temperatures will then be smaller than at high, since the distance r between colliding molecules is greater at low temperatures than at high. The values of the force index deduced in this way from the experimental values of the thermal diffusion factor at various temperatures are summarized in Table V (p. 67).

It is of interest now to see whether these deductions from the thermal diffusion results are consistent with those from other experimental data. Although the coefficient of thermal diffusion is the one most sensitive to the nature of the molecular interactions, the other transport coefficients are dependent to some degree; so too are the coefficients entering into the equation of state. Inferences from thermal diffusion measurements about intermolecular forces should therefore be in agreement with those based on measurements of these other quantities. We shall confine ourselves to a discussion of the viscosity coefficient as being the one most nearly related to the thermal diffusion coefficients.

Comparison with results of viscosity measurements. The Chapman-Enskog theory gives for the coefficient of viscosity, in first approximation,

$$[\mu]_1 = \frac{5kT}{8\Omega^{(2)}(2)},$$

where $\Omega^{(2)}(2)$ is one of the collision integrals already defined (§2.5). Substitution of the value of this integral for the various molecular models shows that for rigid spheres $[\mu]_1 \propto T^{\frac{1}{2}}$, and for molecules which exert an inverse power repulsion $F = \kappa r^{-\nu}$, $[\mu]_1 \propto T^s$ where $s = (\nu+3)/2(\nu-1)$. The value of s, and therefore of ν, can be determined experimentally from the slope of the $\ln \mu \sim \ln T$ curves. A few such curves are shown in fig. 24. It appears that, with the exception of helium, it is characteristic of all gases that the slope of the curve, nearly constant at sufficiently high temperatures, increases as the temperature decreases. The inverse power model is therefore unsatisfactory in accounting for viscosity as it is for thermal diffusion. Again, however, it may be used in the interpretation of the viscosity results if we allow the force index ν to vary with r, that is to say with the temperature. An 'effective' value of the force index at any temperature can then be calculated from the value of $s = d(\ln \mu)/d(\ln T)$

at that temperature, using the above relation between s and v. The experimental curves clearly indicate that, as with thermal diffusion, the effective force index decreases as the temperature decreases. To this extent, then, the thermal diffusion and viscosity results are consistent.

The correlation may be pursued further by comparing the values of the effective force index derived from thermal diffusion measurements with those from viscosity measurements. For this purpose

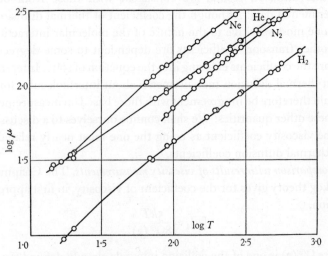

Fig. 24. The temperature dependence of the viscosity of hydrogen, helium, neon and nitrogen. (Viscosity unit: micropoise.)

there are included in Table V values of the force index for the pure components of the mixture to which the thermal diffusion values apply. These have been found from the results which are now available of experimental measurements of viscosity extending over a wide temperature range; for example, those of Trautz and his collaborators (for references see Clark Jones, 1940), the more recent ones of Vasilesco (1945), and at low temperatures those of van Itterbeek and van Paemel (1938, 1940) and of Johnston and Grilly (1942). It is recalled that the thermal diffusion measurements lead to an index of definite significance only when the mixture is isotopic, and it is only in this case that the values of v derived from thermal diffusion and viscosity may be expected to agree. For non-isotopic

TABLE V. *Values of the force index, assuming an inverse power repulsion, deduced from thermal diffusion and from viscosity measurements*

Mixture	Temp. ° K.	R_T	$\tilde{\nu}$	From viscosity	
				ν_1	ν_2
He-Ne	117	0·58	10·0	9·7	14·6
	233	0·64	11·1	12·1	13·6
	585	0·64	11·1	14·2	13·1
He-A	117	0·55	9·1	—	14·6
	233	0·63	10·3	6·3	13·6
	585	0·66	10·8	12·8	13·1
He-Kr	117	0·55	8·9	—	14·6
	233	0·67	10·5	—	13·6
	585	0·67	10·5	—	13·1
He-Xe	233	0·66	10·3	—	13·6
	585	0·66	10·3	6·1	13·1
Ne-A	117	0·28	6·8	—	9·7
	233	0·48	9·2	6·3	12·1
	585	0·57	10·9	12·8	14·2
Ne-Kr	117	0·30	6·8	—	9·7
	233	0·47	8·6	—	12·1
	585	0·64	11·4	—	14·2
Ne-Xe	233	0·46	8·2	—	12·1
	585	0·66	11·2	6·1	14·2
A-Kr	233	0·18	6·0	—	6·3
	585	0·59	11·2	—	12·8
A-Xe	233	0·15	5·8	—	6·3
	585	0·45	8·4	6·1	12·8
H₂-He	117	0·59	11·3	14·6	12·4
	233	0·59	11·3	13·6	12·4
	585	0·59	11·3	13·1	12·4
H₂-N₂	233	0·53	8·6	7·9	12·4
	585	0·60	9·6	13·5	12·4
H₂-CO₂	233	0·35	6·9	5·3	12·4
	585	0·57	9·0	9·0	12·4
Isotopic	—	R_T	ν	ν from viscosity	
²⁰Ne-²²Ne	117	0·37	8·1	9·7	—
	233	0·54	11·1	12·1	—
	585	0·77	18·9	14·2	—
³⁶A-⁴⁰A	117	0·07	5·4	—	—
	233	0·25	6·7	6·3	—
	585	0·48	9·7	12·8	—

mixtures one can find, for the reasons given (p. 45), only an index $\tilde{\nu}$, which is that which would correspond with the experimental value of R_T if the interactions in the mixture were identical. The most that can be expected is that $\tilde{\nu}$ should not be widely different from ν_1 and ν_2, the indices for the component gases, and probably it should lie between them.

It is apparent that, although the values of the index derived from thermal diffusion and from viscosity measurements are alike in showing always a decrease with decreasing temperature, quantitatively the agreement is not good, even for isotopic mixtures where there is no ambiguity about the significance of the index. The discrepancy is larger than would be expected from the experimental error and is possibly another indication of the unsuitability of the molecular model which has been made the basis of the comparison. The tabulated values are of interest in that they give a general picture of the difference in the behaviour of different molecules, but further discussion of the experimental results is now more profitably given in relation to the Lennard-Jones model.

5.4. The Lennard-Jones model

Apart from the evidence just presented, it is clear on general grounds that a model which represents a molecule as a centre of repulsive force only cannot be satisfactory over any extensive range of temperature, for there is ample evidence that the intermolecular force changes with increasing distance between molecules from a repulsion to an attraction. The simplest model which shows this feature of a short-range repulsive force with a long-range attractive force is that used by Lennard-Jones, and the recent work on the evaluation of the collision integrals for molecules of this type is an important advance in the theory of transport phenomena in general and thermal diffusion in particular.

In the Lennard-Jones model the intermolecular force is given by $F = \kappa r^{-\nu} - \kappa' r^{-\nu'}$, and, as we have seen (§2.7), the effect of the attractive component is to make the collision integrals dependent on the temperature. Consequently the thermal diffusion factor is a function of temperature, as it is found to be experimentally, and the question arises as to how far the model can explain the observed variation.

The theoretical results for two special cases of this model have already been discussed (§2.7). Clark Jones (1941) has considered the case of $\nu = 9$, $\nu' = 5$. Hirschfelder, Bird and Spotz (1948) have treated the more probable case of $\nu = 13$, $\nu' = 7$; the attractive force index, $\nu' = 7$, is that required by the quantum-mechanical treatment of molecular interactions and, although the repulsive force index $\nu = 13$ was chosen partly to make the integrals tractable, it is likely that 13 is a more suitable value than 9 for many molecules. It is this (13, 7) case which will now be discussed.

Hirschfelder, Bird and Spotz calculated not the integrals Ω defined above (§2.5), but integrals W related to them by

$$W^{(l)}(n, x) = \frac{1}{\sigma^2} \left[\frac{m_1 m_2}{2\pi k T(m_1 + m_2)} \right]^{\frac{1}{2}} \Omega^{(l)}(n),$$

where $x = \epsilon/kT$, $-\epsilon$ being the minimum potential energy of interaction of two molecules and σ the molecular separation for which the potential energy is zero. σ is thus the collision diameter for low-velocity head-on collisions.

The viscosity coefficient. Following Hirschfelder, Bird and Spotz, we consider first the temperature variation of the viscosity of a simple gas which this model implies. In terms of the integrals W, the first approximation to the coefficient of viscosity (2.7) becomes

$$[\mu]_1 = \frac{5}{16\sigma^2} \left(\frac{mkT}{\pi} \right)^{\frac{1}{2}} \frac{1}{W^{(2)}(2)},$$

and the exact value is $V[\mu]_1$, where V is a slowly varying function of kT/ϵ, the value of which Hirschfelder, Bird and Spotz have calculated. Thus μ can be found as a function of kT/ϵ.

A direct comparison of these theoretical values with experimental ones requires a knowledge of the values of ϵ/k and σ. These quantities can be determined from the second virial coefficient at different temperatures, but the values so found are not very accurate, and Hirschfelder, Bird and Spotz have therefore proceeded by finding from the experimental values of the viscosity and the theoretical expression those values of ϵ/k and σ which give the best agreement. Some of these values are shown in Table VI, and a comparison of the experimental and theoretical values of the viscosity of a few gases is made in Table VII. It will be seen that with proper choice

TABLE VI. *Values of the force constants ϵ/k and σ based on viscosity measurements and the (13, 7) model; also values determined from the second virial coefficient (from Hirschfelder, Bird and Spotz, 1949)*

Gas	From viscosity		From second virial coefficient	
	ϵ/k (°K.)	σ (A.)	ϵ/k (°K.)	σ (A.)
He	6·03	2·70	6·03	2·63
Ne	35·7	2·80	35·7	2·74
A	124·0	3·418	119·5	3·41
H_2	33·3	2·968	37·02	2·92
N_2	91·46	3·681	95·9	3·72
CO_2	190	3·996	185	4·57

TABLE VII. *The temperature variation of the viscosity: experimental, and theoretical values for the (13, 7) model (from Hirschfelder, Bird and Spotz, 1948)*

T°K.	Hydrogen $\epsilon/k=33\cdot3°$ $\sigma=2\cdot968$A. $\mu\times10^7$		Nitrogen $\epsilon/k=91\cdot46°$ $\sigma=3\cdot681$A. $\mu\times10^7$		Argon $\epsilon/k=124\cdot0°$ $\sigma=3\cdot418$A. $\mu\times10^7$		Neon $\epsilon/k=35\cdot7°$ $\sigma=2\cdot70$A. $\mu\times10^7$	
	Exp.	Calc.	Exp.	Calc.	Exp.	Calc.	Exp.	Calc.
80	—	—	—	—	688	649	1198	1212
100	421	416	698	687	839	814	1435	1451
120	481	477	826	820	993	979	1646	1665
140	535	533	948	947	1146	1142	1841	1867
160	585	586	1068	1070	1298	1300	2026	2054
180	634	635	1183	1186	1447	1454	2204	2231
200	681	683	1295	1296	1594	1601	2376	2396
220	727	728	1403	1402	1739	1744	2544	2558
240	771	773	1505	1503	1878	1882	2708	2713
260	814	815	1603	1600	2014	2014	2867	2862
280	856	856	1696	1693	2145	2143	3021	3008
300	896	896	1786	1785	2270	2269	3173	3149
400	1127	1073	2270	2202	—	—	—	—
500	1305	1237	2657	2570	—	—	—	—
800	1744	1689	{ 3493 3610	3528	4621	4641	5918	5945
1000	1987	1958	{ 4011 4066	4068	5302	5391	6800	6872
1200	2205	2199	{ 4452 4613	4554	5947	6083	—	—
1500	2496	2542	{ 5050 5247	5268	6778	6983	—	—

of ϵ/k and σ, the $(13, 7)$ model does in fact represent the viscosity of many gases remarkably well.

The coefficient of concentration diffusion. Hirschfelder, Bird and Spotz have used the values of the force constants thus determined from viscosity data to calculate the coefficient of concentration diffusion. The theoretical expression (2.8) for this coefficient becomes in terms of the integrals W

$$[D_{12}]_1 = \frac{3}{16n}\left[\frac{kT}{2\pi m_0 M_1 M_2}\right]^{\frac{1}{2}} \frac{1}{\sigma_{12}^2 W_{12}^{(1)}(1)}.$$

This reduces for the case of self-diffusion to

$$[D_{11}]_1 = \frac{3}{16n}\left(\frac{kT}{\pi m_1}\right)^{\frac{1}{2}} \frac{1}{\sigma_1^2 W_1^{(1)}(1)},$$

for there is now no distinction between the properties of the two species of molecule, (1) and (2). The theoretical values of D_{11} calculated from this expression were found to agree with values deduced from experimental measurements of the diffusion of isotopes. This agreement has been confirmed by Winn (1950), who has made diffusion measurements over an extensive temperature range. A selection of his results is given in Table VIII.

TABLE VIII. *Experimental values of the coefficient of self-diffusion,* D_{11}, *and theoretical values for the* $(13, 7)$ *model (from Winn 1950)*

Temp. °K.	Neon		Argon		Nitrogen	
	D_{11} (exp.)	D_{11} (calc.)	D_{11} (exp.)	D_{11} (calc.)	D_{11} (exp.)	D_{11} (calc.)
353·1	0·703	0·668	0·249	0·246	0·287	0·273
298·1	0·516	0·504	0·178	0·178	0·212	0·203
273·1	0·452	0·435	0·156	0·154	0·185	0·174
194·6	0·255	0·246	0·083	0·082	0·104	0·0946
77·6	0·049	0·049	0·013	0·013	0·0168	0·0161

The expression for D_{12} above involves the force constants of dissimilar molecules only. These constants can therefore be determined from experimental values of D_{12} at different temperatures, just as the force constants for the interaction of like molecules were determined from viscosity measurements. Unfortunately, experimental values of D_{12} over a range of temperature are rare, but it is possible to evaluate ϵ_{12}/k from a value of D_{12} at a single temperature if the reasonable assumption is made that $\sigma_{12} = \frac{1}{2}(\sigma_1 + \sigma_2)$. Some values calculated in this way by Hirschfelder, Bird and Spotz are shown in Table IX. This table includes also the geometric mean of the values of ϵ_1/k and ϵ_2/k deduced from the viscosity of the pure gases. It will be seen that in many cases the geometric mean, $(\epsilon_1\epsilon_2)^{\frac{1}{2}}$, is a fair approximation to ϵ_{12}. This relation, which is supported by other experimental results (cf. Hirschfelder and Roseveare, 1939), and which has some theoretical basis (Clark Jones, 1941), is made use of later.

TABLE IX. *Force constants for unlike molecules (from Hirschfelder, Bird and Spotz, 1949)*

Mixture	D_{12} exp. (cm.²/sec.)	Temp. for D_{12} (°K.)	Arith. mean σ_{12}, from viscosity (A.)	Geom. mean ϵ_{12}/k, from viscosity (°K.)	ϵ_{12}/k from D_{12} (°K.)
H_2-N_2	0·674	273·2	3·325	55·2	47·8
H_2-A	0·77	293·2	3·193	64·3	64·1
H_2-CO_2	0·550	273·2	3·482	79·5	76·0
He-Ne	—	—	2·75	14·7	—
He-A	0·641	273·2	3·059	27·3	24·5
Ne-A	—	—	3·11	66·5	—

5.41. The thermal diffusion factor

The various ratios (2.9) which enter into the expression for the thermal diffusion factor are, in terms of the integrals W,

$$A = \frac{W_{12}^{(2)}(2)}{5W_{12}^{(1)}(1)}, \quad B = \frac{5W_{12}^{(1)}(2) - W_{12}^{(1)}(3)}{5W_{12}^{(1)}(1)}, \quad C = \frac{2W_{12}^{(1)}(2)}{5W_{12}^{(1)}(1)},$$

$$E_1 = \frac{2A}{(1-M)^{\frac{1}{2}}x_{12}}, \quad E_2 = \frac{2A}{(1+M)^{\frac{1}{2}}x_{21}},$$

where $x_{12} = \left(\dfrac{\sigma_{12}}{\sigma_1}\right)^2 \dfrac{W_{12}^{(2)}(2)}{W_1^{(2)}(2)}$, and x_{21} is given by a similar expression. Values of the thermal diffusion factor for isotopic mixtures can be readily found from these ratios, since for such mixtures

$W_1 = W_2 = W_{12}$, and $\sigma_1 = \sigma_2 = \sigma_{12}$. An immediate comparison of theoretical and experimental values can therefore be made. For non-isotopic mixtures we may proceed as in the previous case of the simple inverse power repulsive force and compare the experimental values of the thermal separation ratio R_T with theoretical values for an isotopic mixture of the same mass ratio (cf. Grew, 1949). A better procedure is that of Hirschfelder, Bird and Spotz (1949), who, starting from the values of ϵ/k and σ for the pure gases found from viscosity data as explained above, have deduced from them the value of ϵ_{12}/k making use of the approximate relations $\epsilon_{12} = (\epsilon_1 \epsilon_2)^{\frac{1}{2}}$ and $\sigma_{12} = \frac{1}{2}(\sigma_1 + \sigma_2)$, and so calculated the ratios $A \ldots E$ and the thermal diffusion factor from (2.12).*

The theoretical values of the thermal diffusion factor α thus found, when plotted as a function of kT/ϵ_{12}, yield curves of the same general form as those for isotopic mixtures shown in fig. 10. In comparing these theoretical values of α and R_T with experimental ones it should be remembered that the theoretical values are first approximations—no attempt has been made to apply a correction as was done in the case of the simple inverse power repulsion model. The exact values are probably greater, perhaps by as much as 10 %.

The inert gas mixtures: non-isotopic. Some theoretical and experimental values of R_T are shown in fig. 25, and more fully in Appendix 5, Table IV A. The comparison shows that the $(13, 7)$ model is remarkably successful in representing the temperature variation of the thermal diffusion factor; in some cases, such as neon-argon, the discrepancy between the experimental and theoretical values is not much greater than the experimental error. It appears, however, that at the higher temperatures the theoretical values generally exceed the experimental ones and that therefore the index 13 for the repulsive force is probably too great.

Isotopic mixtures

Neon and argon. The promise given by the comparison of the theoretical and experimental results for the inert gas mixtures that the Lennard-Jones $(13, 7)$ model, or a slight modification of it, would prove adequate is only partially supported by the results

---

* In their paper, Hirschfelder, Bird and Spotz (1949) give not α but R_T; they have, however, made an error in the final step in which R_T is found from α (cf. Grew, 1950, *J. Chem. Phys.* **18**, 149).

first obtained for isotopic mixtures. As we have seen, Nier and Stier conclude that, for isotopic mixtures of neon and argon, the experimental value of R_T is a linear function of $\ln T$. For argon, such a relation approximates fairly well, over the relevant temperature range, to the theoretical curve for the $(13, 7)$ case; but for neon the experimental measurements extend to temperatures at

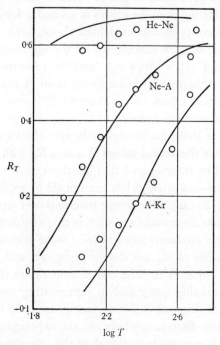

Fig. 25. The temperature variation of the thermal separation ratio R_T for helium-neon, neon-argon, and argon-krypton mixtures. ○ experimental values (Grew, 1947); — theoretical curve for $(13, 7)$ model.

which, theoretically, R_T should be sensibly constant. Fig. 26 shows the experimental and theoretical values for these two mixtures. It is desirable that the rather difficult experimental measurements at the higher temperatures be repeated.

Hydrogen-deuterium. The measurements made by de Troyer, van Itterbeek and Rietveld (1951) at temperatures below 90° K., with those made earlier at higher temperatures, show that the behaviour of the thermal diffusion factor in hydrogen-deuterium is essentially similar to that in other mixtures. The values of R_T obtained experimentally at low temperatures are, however, considerably greater than those for the (13, 7) model, as is seen in Table III, p. 53; on the other hand the temperature at which R_T changes sign agrees fairly closely with the theoretical value.

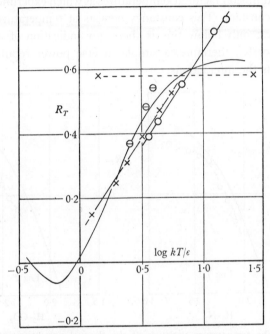

Fig. 26. The temperature variation of the thermal separation ratio R_T for isotopic mixtures. — theoretical curve for (13, 7) model; −O−O− experimental values for ^{20}Ne-^{22}Ne (Stier, 1942); −×−×− experimental values for ^{36}A-^{40}A (Stier, 1942); ⊖−⊖ experimental values for $^{16}O^{16}O$-$^{16}O^{18}O$ (Whalley, Winter and Briscoe, 1949); × −−−− × experimental values for H_2-He mixture.

Isotopic oxygen, nitrogen and methane. The values of R_T for these mixtures, given in Table IV, p. 54, are in good agreement with the theoretical ones for the (13, 7) model, given in the same table. The results for oxygen are shown graphically in fig. 26.

Isotopic ammonia. The ammonia molecule being polar, the inter-actions are more complex than those of non-polar molecules, and even approximate agreement between the theoretical values for the (13, 7) model and experimental ones is hardly to be expected.

The reversal of sign of R_T does, however, occur at a temperature near that required by the (13, 7) model.

Other mixtures

Hydrogen-helium mixtures. The (13, 7) model is here not satisfactory, for, as fig. 26 shows, it requires a marked variation in the thermal diffusion factor at temperatures at which experiment shows it to be constant. This constancy persists at temperatures as low as 20° K.; only below this is there any indication of a change. Above 20° K., therefore, a simple inverse power repulsion best represents the interactions.

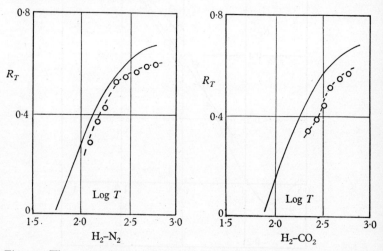

Fig. 27. The temperature variation of the thermal separation ratio R_T for hydrogen-nitrogen and hydrogen-carbon dioxide mixtures. — theoretical values for (13, 7) model; O experimental values.

Hydrogen-nitrogen and hydrogen-carbon dioxide mixtures. The experimental and theoretical results for the (13, 7) model are compared in fig. 27. The discrepancy between them suggests that a Lennard-Jones model with repulsive force index less than 13 would be more suitable. For hydrogen-carbon dioxide mixtures the variation of R_T with temperature is similar to that observed in other mixtures, and there is no indication that the behaviour of these mixtures is exceptional as was once suggested.

These results suggest that with force indices suitably chosen, the Lennard-Jones model could account satisfactorily for the observed behaviour of most gases in thermal diffusion. For the coefficients of viscosity and concentration diffusion the special case of the (13, 7) model gives apparently good agreement in many cases. It is, however, the thermal diffusion factor which is most sensitive to the nature of the molecular interactions, and the comparison which has been made above of the theoretical and experimental values of this coefficient indicates that, although the (13, 7) model is satisfactory in several cases, in others a smaller value of the repulsive force index would probably be more suitable. There is clearly a need for more experimental results, especially those relating to isotopic mixtures, and for theoretical values for cases of the Lennard-Jones model other than those few which have been treated so far. When these are available it seems likely that the force constants may be determined with some exactness.

CHAPTER VI

THE DIFFUSION THERMOEFFECT

6.1. Introduction

In 1873 Dufour published a paper entitled 'On the diffusion of gases through porous partitions and the accompanying temperature changes'. In the experiments there described, a porous vessel, in which a sensitive thermometer was inserted, was contained within another vessel. The interior of the porous vessel was in communication through a glass tube with the atmosphere so that the pressure within it was constant. When this inner vessel was filled with air, and hydrogen was circulated in the space between the two vessels, Dufour observed that as the hydrogen diffused into the inner vessel the thermometer indicated a fall in temperature. He found a similar effect when the porous vessel was initially filled with carbon dioxide and air was circulated about it. Dufour expressed the view that the temperature changes occur, not throughout the gas but near the surface of the porous partition. In this way he discovered what has since come to be called the diffusion thermoeffect; the possibility of such an effect is contained in the Chapman-Enskog theory of non-uniform gases, but it is only recently that its experimental investigation has been pursued.

The diffusion thermoeffect can be easily demonstrated. The porous diaphragm used by Dufour is not essential and is an unnecessary complication. In a form of apparatus described by Miller (1949) a glass cylinder about 7 cm. in diameter and 24 cm. in length has across one end an iris diaphragm. Through a plug closing the other end passes a tube carrying a support for, and leads to, a fine platinum wire (0·02 mm. diameter) which serves as a resistance thermometer. The wire is placed a few millimetres distant from the diaphragm. The cylinder, in a vertical position with the diaphragm below, is filled with hydrogen. On opening the diaphragm air diffuses into the hydrogen, and a galvanometer in the bridge circuit of which the platinum wire is a part shows a momentary deflexion, indicating an increase in temperature.

The diffusion thermoeffect consists in a transport of heat as part of the process of diffusion in a gas mixture; it is therefore associated with the existence of a concentration gradient. The effect is intimately connected with thermal diffusion, the molecular transport associated with a temperature gradient. A study of the diffusion thermoeffect can therefore yield information about the thermal diffusion factor which is a supplement to that obtained from the thermal diffusion measurements discussed in the preceding chapters. The experimental work is mainly due to Waldmann (1943–9), who has developed a method of measuring the effect at various temperatures and pressures, and determined from his results values of the thermal diffusion factor for a number of mixtures.

6.2. The theory of the effect

As we have seen, the Chapman-Enskog theory leads to the result that the particle flux through a surface at rest in a gas mixture in which the temperature is not uniform has two components, one due to the concentration gradient, the other to the temperature gradient. The theory shows also that the energy flux in a non-uniform gas likewise has two components.

An expression for the energy flux through a surface moving with the mean velocity of a gas mixture has already been given (2.6). In terms of the thermal diffusion factor it is

$$\mathbf{q} = -\lambda \frac{\partial T}{\partial \mathbf{r}} + nkT\alpha n_{10} n_{20} (\bar{\mathbf{C}}_1 - \bar{\mathbf{C}}_2).$$

The first term represents the heat flux due to conduction, the second a flux due to diffusion, since it depends on the difference of the mean velocities of the two components. It follows from this equation that if two gases initially at the same temperature interdiffuse there is a transport of heat, with a consequent development of a temperature gradient. Comparison of this equation for the heat flux with the diffusion equation (2.3) shows that the direction of this temperature gradient is such that the thermal diffusion which results from it opposes the diffusion to which the gradient is due. For example, if hydrogen diffuses into nitrogen, the temperature rises where the hydrogen is in excess and falls where the nitrogen is in excess.

In finding an expression for the temperature change which accompanies diffusion, and which is of course the quantity measured experimentally, we start from the expression for the energy flux relative to a surface stationary in the frame to which the molecular velocities are referred. This flux is greater than the above by a term $(\tfrac{5}{2})nkT\bar{\mathbf{c}}$ which represents the energy transport due to the general motion of the gas. Thus

$$\mathbf{q} = -\lambda\frac{\partial T}{\partial \mathbf{r}} + nkT\alpha n_{10}n_{20}(\bar{\mathbf{C}}_1 - \bar{\mathbf{C}}_2) + \tfrac{5}{2}nkT\bar{\mathbf{c}}. \qquad (6.1)$$

We assume that the pressure p of the gas is steady and uniform. If Q is the energy density in the gas, the conservation of energy requires that

$$\frac{\partial Q}{\partial t} + \frac{\partial}{\partial \mathbf{r}}.\mathbf{q} = 0,$$

where $(\partial/\partial\mathbf{r}).\mathbf{q}$ is the divergence of $\mathbf{q}$. Now $Q = (\tfrac{3}{2})nkT = (\tfrac{3}{2})p$, if a small term involving the mean velocity of the gas is neglected. Since p is steady,

$$\frac{\partial}{\partial \mathbf{r}}.\mathbf{q} = 0;$$

and substituting for q from (1)

$$\frac{\partial}{\partial \mathbf{r}}.\left[-\lambda\frac{\partial T}{\partial \mathbf{r}} + nkT\alpha n_{10}n_{20}(\bar{\mathbf{C}}_1 - \bar{\mathbf{C}}_2) + \tfrac{5}{2}nkT\bar{\mathbf{c}}\right] = 0;$$

or, assuming λ and αT to be independent of position,

$$\lambda\frac{\partial}{\partial \mathbf{r}}.\frac{\partial T}{\partial \mathbf{r}} = kT\alpha\frac{\partial}{\partial \mathbf{r}}.[nn_{10}n_{20}(\bar{\mathbf{C}}_1 - \bar{\mathbf{C}}_2)] + \tfrac{5}{2}nkT\frac{\partial}{\partial \mathbf{r}}.\bar{\mathbf{c}}.$$

Now $(\bar{\mathbf{C}}_1 - \bar{\mathbf{C}}_2) = (n/n_2)\bar{\mathbf{C}}_1$, therefore

$$\lambda\frac{\partial}{\partial \mathbf{r}}.\frac{\partial T}{\partial \mathbf{r}} = \alpha kT\frac{\partial}{\partial \mathbf{r}}.(n_1\bar{\mathbf{C}}_1) + \tfrac{5}{2}nkT\frac{\partial}{\partial \mathbf{r}}.\bar{\mathbf{c}}. \qquad (6.2)$$

We now find expressions for $\dfrac{\partial}{\partial \mathbf{r}}.(n_1\bar{\mathbf{C}}_1)$ and $\dfrac{\partial}{\partial \mathbf{r}}.\bar{\mathbf{c}}$, using the equations expressing the constancy of number for molecules of the first kind alone and of both kinds together.

The flux density of molecules of both kinds through a stationary surface is $n\bar{\mathbf{c}}$; hence constancy of total number requires that

$$\frac{\partial n}{\partial t} + \frac{\partial}{\partial \mathbf{r}}.(n\bar{\mathbf{c}}) = 0.$$

Therefore
$$\frac{\partial}{\partial \mathbf{r}}\cdot\bar{\mathbf{c}} = -\frac{1}{n}\frac{\partial n}{\partial t} - \frac{1}{n}\bar{\mathbf{c}}\cdot\frac{\partial n}{\partial \mathbf{r}} = -\frac{1}{n}\frac{Dn}{Dt},$$

where
$$\frac{D}{Dt} = \frac{\partial}{\partial t} + \bar{\mathbf{c}}\cdot\frac{\partial}{\partial \mathbf{r}}.$$

Since the pressure $p = nkT$ is constant,
$$\frac{\partial}{\partial \mathbf{r}}\cdot\bar{\mathbf{c}} = \frac{1}{T}\frac{DT}{Dt}.$$

Considering the first species of molecules only, the flux density is $n_1\bar{\mathbf{c}}_1 = n_1(\bar{\mathbf{C}}_1 + \bar{\mathbf{c}})$, and therefore

$$\frac{\partial n_1}{\partial t} + \frac{\partial}{\partial \mathbf{r}}\cdot n_1(\bar{\mathbf{C}}_1 + \bar{\mathbf{c}}) = 0,$$

or
$$\frac{\partial n_1}{\partial t} + \bar{\mathbf{c}}\cdot\frac{\partial n_1}{\partial \mathbf{r}} + n_1\frac{\partial}{\partial \mathbf{r}}\cdot\bar{\mathbf{c}} + \frac{\partial}{\partial \mathbf{r}}\cdot(n_1\bar{\mathbf{C}}_1) = 0,$$

or
$$\frac{\partial}{\partial \mathbf{r}}\cdot(n_1\bar{\mathbf{C}}_1) = -\left(\frac{Dn_1}{Dt} + n_1\frac{\partial}{\partial \mathbf{r}}\cdot\bar{\mathbf{c}}\right) = -\frac{Dn_1}{Dt} + \frac{n_1}{n}\frac{Dn}{Dt}.$$

Therefore
$$\frac{\partial}{\partial \mathbf{r}}\cdot(n_1\bar{\mathbf{C}}_1) = -n\frac{Dn_{10}}{Dt}.$$

Substituting in (2) gives

$$\lambda\frac{\partial}{\partial \mathbf{r}}\cdot\frac{\partial T}{\partial \mathbf{r}} + \alpha kTn\frac{Dn_{10}}{Dt} = \tfrac{5}{2}nk\frac{DT}{Dt},$$

or
$$\lambda\frac{\partial}{\partial \mathbf{r}}\cdot\frac{\partial T}{\partial \mathbf{r}} + \alpha p\frac{Dn_{10}}{Dt} = \rho c_p\frac{DT}{Dt}, \qquad (6.3)$$

where $c_p = (\tfrac{5}{2})nk$ is the specific heat at constant pressure and ρ is the density of the gas.

The 'non-stationary' case. This general equation reduces to a simpler form when the mean velocity of the gas is zero—a condition which was fulfilled in Waldmann's first experiments. Now $D/Dt = \partial/\partial t$, and the equation becomes

$$\lambda\frac{\partial}{\partial \mathbf{r}}\cdot\frac{\partial T}{\partial \mathbf{r}} + \alpha p\frac{\partial n_{10}}{\partial t} = \rho c_p\frac{\partial T}{\partial t},$$

or
$$\frac{\partial T}{\partial t} = K\frac{\partial}{\partial \mathbf{r}}\cdot\frac{\partial T}{\partial \mathbf{r}} + \beta\frac{\partial n_{10}}{\partial t}, \qquad (6.4)$$

where $K = \lambda/\rho c_p$, the temperature diffusivity, and $\beta = \alpha p/\rho c_p$. Also we have

$$\frac{\partial n_{10}}{\partial t} = D_{12} \frac{\partial}{\partial \mathbf{r}} \cdot \frac{\partial n_{10}}{\partial \mathbf{r}}, \qquad (6.5)$$

assuming that the temperature gradient due to diffusion is so small that thermal diffusion is negligible.

In finding solutions to equations (6.4) and (6.5), Waldmann considers first the ideal case of a gas mixture enclosed between two parallel plates of infinite extent. Let the plates be in the xy-plane at $z = +l$ and $z = -l$ respectively. At $z = 0$ is a diaphragm which can be removed when desired. The pressure is supposed everywhere to be the same, but the composition of the mixture above the diaphragm is different from that below, so that when the diaphragm is withdrawn, diffusion occurs. Let the initial proportion of the heavier molecules in the mixture be $n_{10}^0 + \delta n_{10}^0$ below the diaphragm, and $n_{10}^0 - \delta n_{10}^0$ above, the composition of the mixture ultimately changing to n_{10}^0 everywhere. The initial temperature throughout is T_0. As diffusion occurs the composition and temperature at the position $z = 0$ remain constant at n_{10}^0 and T_0. At the plates the particle flux vanishes and so too does the energy flux if we assume adiabatic conditions. The boundary conditions are therefore

$$\left(\frac{\partial n_{10}}{\partial z}\right)_{z = \pm l} = \left(\frac{\partial T}{\partial z}\right)_{z = \pm l} = 0.$$

The solution of the equations, subject to these conditions, is shown graphically in fig. 28, where the dimensionless quantities

$$\xi = \frac{z}{l}, \quad \tau = \frac{\pi D_{12}^2}{4l^2} t, \quad \theta = \frac{T_0 - T}{\beta \delta n_{10}^0},$$

have been introduced. The curves show the variation of the temperature with position and time in the special case when $D_{12} = K$, a relation which holds approximately in several mixtures. It will be seen that the maximum temperature change occurs at the boundary ($\xi = 1$) at the time $\tau = 1$. The changes at corresponding points on either side of the plane $z = 0$ are equal but opposite, so that a temperature gradient is established across the plane; this gradient is in such a direction as to bring about thermal diffusion in opposition to the concentration diffusion process which generates the gradient, that is, normally the temperature of the denser gas falls while that of the lighter gas rises. As an example of the magnitude of the temperature changes to be expected in an actual case, Waldmann considers the diffusion of one pure gas into an equal volume of another, so that $\delta n_{10}^0 = 0.5$. For hydrogen diffusing into nitrogen at room temperature the maximum difference in

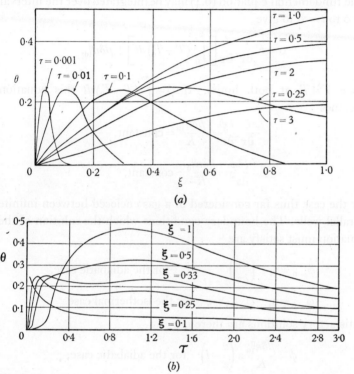

Fig. 28. The temperature change θ as a function of (a) time τ at various positions ξ in the diffusion vessel; (b) position ξ at various times τ. (After Waldmann, 1943.)

temperature at two points close to, but on opposite sides of, the $z = 0$ plane is about 7°C.; for hydrogen diffusing into deuterium it is about 0.5°C. These values were calculated using the known values of the thermal diffusion factor α. The changes are thus appreciable, and their measurement offers a means of determining the thermal diffusion factor for a gas mixture.

These results apply to the case when the bounding walls are adiabatic. Experimentally it is more convenient to deal with the isothermal case, in which the temperature of the gas adjacent to the walls remains constant at T_0. A treatment similar to that given for the adiabatic case is difficult, but a different development is possible which leads to results for both the adiabatic and isothermal cases, and which are directly applicable in an experimental investigation. The fundamental equation (6.4) may be integrated over the interval $t = 0$ to $t = \infty$ to give

$$0 = K \frac{\partial}{\partial \mathbf{r}} \cdot \frac{\partial}{\partial \mathbf{r}} \left[\int_0^\infty (T - T_0)\, dt \right] + \beta \delta n_{10}^0,$$

since $T = T_0$ at both limits. If $\phi = \int_0^\infty (T - T_0)\, dt$ this equation becomes

$$\frac{\partial}{\partial \mathbf{r}} \cdot \frac{\partial \phi}{\partial \mathbf{r}} = \frac{\beta \delta n_{10}^0}{K} = \text{constant},$$

or

$$\frac{\partial^2 \phi}{\partial z^2} = \frac{\beta \delta n_{10}^0}{K} = \text{constant},$$

for the case thus far considered of a gas enclosed between infinite parallel walls. The boundary conditions which the solution of the equation must satisfy are

$$\phi_{z=0} = 0, \quad \left(\frac{\partial \phi}{\partial z} \right)_{z = \pm l} = 0 \quad \text{for the adiabatic case},$$

$$\phi_{z=0} = 0, \quad \phi_{z = \pm l} = 0 \quad \text{for the isothermal case}.$$

Satisfactory solutions are therefore

$$\phi = \frac{\beta \delta n_{10}^0}{K} z \left(\frac{z}{2} - l \right) \quad \text{for the adiabatic case},$$

$$\phi = \frac{\beta \delta n_{10}^0}{K} \frac{z}{2} (z - l) \quad \text{for the isothermal case}.$$

ϕ is the area under a curve of fig. 28 a; it can be determined experimentally, and from it β and hence α, the thermal diffusion factor, can be found. This is the principle of Waldmann's first method of determining α.

The 'stationary' case. When the interdiffusing gases are in motion, say in the z direction, with mean velocity $\overline{w}$, and conditions are steady,

$$\frac{D}{Dt} = \overline{w} \frac{\partial}{\partial z},$$

and equation (3) becomes

$$\lambda \frac{\partial}{\partial \mathbf{r}} \cdot \frac{\partial T}{\partial \mathbf{r}} + \alpha p \overline{w} \frac{\partial n_{10}}{\partial z} = \rho c_p \overline{w} \frac{\partial T}{\partial z}. \tag{6.6}$$

The pressure p is uniform and therefore $\overline{w}$ is approximately independent of z. If equation (6.6) is now integrated over the range $z = -\infty$ to $z = +\infty$ we obtain, assuming $\partial T/\partial z = 0$ at $z = \pm\infty$,

$$\lambda \frac{\partial}{\partial \mathbf{r}} \cdot \frac{\partial \psi}{\partial \mathbf{r}} + \alpha p \overline{w}(n_{10}'' - n_{10}') = 0,$$

where $\psi = \int_{-\infty}^{+\infty} (T - T_0)\, dz$, T_0 being the value of T at $z = \pm\infty$, and n_{10}'', n_{10}' being the values of n_{10} at $z = +\infty$ and $z = -\infty$ respectively. Hence

$$\lambda \left(\frac{\partial^2 \psi}{\partial x^2} + \frac{\partial^2 \psi}{\partial y^2} \right) + \alpha p \overline{w}(n_{10}'' - n_{10}') = 0.$$

Treating λ, α, p and n_{10} as independent of x and y, ψ can be found as a function of x and y, just as the integral ϕ was found as a function of z in the previous, non-stationary, case. Thus from a measurement of ψ and the difference in composition $(n_{10}'' - n_{10}')$, together with a knowledge of $\overline{w}$ and the conductivity λ, the thermal diffusion factor α can be determined.

In these methods of determining the thermal diffusion factor, however, account must be taken of the fact that when the inter-diffusing gases are imperfect there is, in addition to the diffusion thermoeffect, a heat transport due to the imperfect nature of the gases. Waldmann has shown that for mixtures such as hydrogen-nitrogen, for which the thermal diffusion factor is large, this additional transport is only about 1 % of the diffusion thermoeffect, but in other cases, for example, argon-carbon dioxide mixtures, it may even exceed the diffusion thermoeffect. Fortunately, the additional transport is dependent on the pressure, whereas the diffusion thermoeffect is nearly independent. From measurements made at different pressures, therefore, it is possible to determine the true thermoeffect.

In deriving the thermal diffusion factor α from the temperature changes, a knowledge of the thermal conductivity of the mixture is required, and this is a disadvantage of this method of determining α as compared with that depending on a measurement of the thermal separation. On the other hand, this method yields values of α at a definite temperature, and the sensitivity is independent of composition so that values of α for mixtures in which one component is rare can be obtained without difficulty.

6.3. The experimental measurement of the diffusion thermo-effect

For the measurement of the diffusion thermoeffect Waldmann has used two methods corresponding respectively with the non-stationary and the stationary case considered above. In the first the

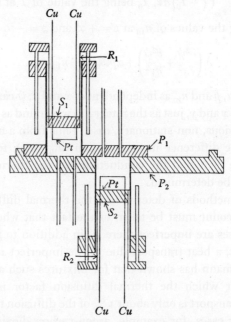

Fig. 29. Waldmann's (1947a) apparatus for the measurement of the transient temperature changes during diffusion.

nterdiffusing gases as a whole are at rest, and the transient temperature changes which occur in them are recorded. In the other, the gases flow in parallel contiguous streams, and the difference in the steady mean temperatures along flow lines in each stream, set up as the gases interdiffuse, is measured.

The apparatus used for the first mode of experiment is shown in fig. 29. The diffusion vessel consisted of two brass cylinders of internal diameter 4 cm. soldered into brass plates P_1, P_2. Sliding within these cylinders were the tubes R_1, R_2, themselves closed by plates S_1, S_2. Two cylindrical enclosures of variable height were thus formed, and into them were put the pure gases or gas mixtures which were later to interdiffuse. The apparatus is shown in the position for filling. By turning the upper plate P_1, the upper chamber was then brought above the lower and diffusion began. The ensuing temperature changes were measured by means of platinum wires Pt connected between copper leads as shown. The wires, each of 0·015 mm. diameter, 3·4 cm. length, and resistance 19 ohms, lay along a diameter of the cylinder; they could be inserted in turn in one arm of a Wheatstone bridge. The deflexion of the bridge galvanometer was recorded photographically as a function of the time.

The conditions here differ from those postulated in the theoretical discussion above, since the gases are confined within cylindrical walls. The instantaneous temperature consequently varies along the diametral platinum filament. Waldmann has shown, however, that the thermal diffusion factor is, in these experimental conditions, proportional to the time integral of the *mean* temperature change along the filament, that is, to $\int_0^\infty \overline{(T-T_0)}\, dt$; further, this integral is itself proportional to the time integral of the galvanometer deflexion. The thermal diffusion factor can therefore be calculated from the recorded galvanometer deflexion-time curve. It is of interest that the coefficient of concentration diffusion D_{12} also can be derived from the same curve, as Waldmann has shown.

The second method was developed so that measurements could be made at various temperatures. Here the gases are caused to flow with equal velocities through two holes, parallel and contiguous, bored in a brass rod (fig. 30). The two holes, A, B, communicate through a gauze-covered slit, G, and along the axis of each is a platinum wire, P, which serves to measure the mean axial temperature. The rod can be immersed in a refrigerant contained within a vacuum vessel. The gases which are to diffuse are led in through the tubes C, D. Diffusion across the slit as the gases move along gives rise to a steady temperature difference between corresponding points on opposite sides of the slit, and from the mean

axial temperature difference the thermal diffusion factor can be
calculated. In this way Waldmann has investigated the dependence
of the thermal diffusion factor on temperature in a number of
mixtures.

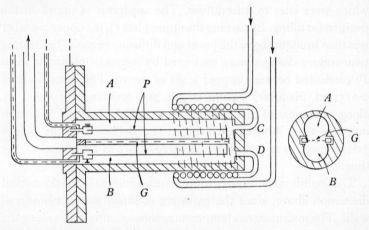

Fig. 30. Waldmann's (1949) apparatus for the measurement of the steady
difference in temperature in interdiffusing streams. A, B, holes in brass block
communicating through G, gauze-covered slit; P, platinum wires for measuring
temperature; C, D, gas inlets.

6.4. Experimental results

With his first apparatus Waldmann examined a number of
mixtures, without, however, making a correction in evaluating the
thermal diffusion factor for the heat transport due to the imperfection of the gases. For hydrogen-nitrogen and hydrogen-
deuterium mixtures the necessary correction is negligible; results
for hydrogen-nitrogen mixtures were obtained by interdiffusion of
adjacent mixtures in the series in which the proportion of nitrogen
had the values $n_{10}^0 = 0.0$, 0.2, 0.4, 0.6, 0.8, 1.0, so that δn_{10}^0 had the
value 0.1; for hydrogen-deuterium the pure gases interdiffused, so
that $\delta n_{10}^0 = 0.5$. All measurements were made at about $293°$ K. The
results are shown in fig. 31, which includes also some values derived
from thermal diffusion measurements. For hydrogen-nitrogen, and
indeed for most mixtures for which results have been obtained by
both methods, the agreement is satisfactory. Hydrogen-deuterium
mixtures are exceptional in showing a relatively large discrepancy.
Waldmann's results confirm the conclusion already drawn (§5.1)

that α diminishes with increasing proportion of the heavier component of the mixture.

By the second method Waldmann has investigated the dependence of the thermal diffusion factor on temperature. In this series of

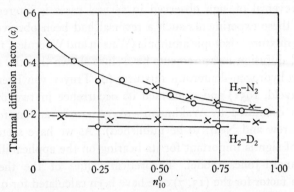

Fig. 31. The variation of the thermal diffusion factor with composition. n_{10}^0, volume fraction of nitrogen or deuterium; —○— Waldmann's results (from diffusion thermoeffect); —×— Ibbs's results (from thermal diffusion).

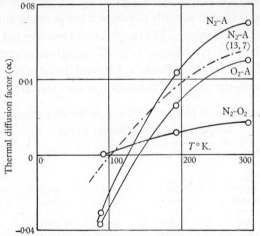

Fig. 32. The variation of the thermal diffusion factor with temperature. –○– Waldmann's results; — – — theoretical values for the (13, 7) model.

measurements observations were made at different pressures, so that by extrapolation to zero pressure the effect of the imperfection of the gases could be eliminated and the diffusion thermoeffect properly determined. His results are given in Table X, and some of them graphically in fig. 32. In all cases, with one exception, viz. argon-carbon dioxide, the thermal diffusion factor diminishes with decreasing temperature; Waldmann's results thus confirm satisfactorily those obtained by measurements of the thermal diffusion effect.

The reversal of sign observed in several cases is interesting. Prior to these experiments such a reversal had been observed in only one mixture—isotopic ammonia (Watson and Woernley, 1943). Thermal diffusion measurements have since shown that the effect occurs in hydrogen-deuterium mixtures (de Troyer, van Itterbeek and Rietveld, 1951) and confirmed its occurrence in two of the mixtures examined by Waldmann—oxygen-argon and nitrogen-argon (Grew and Neal: to be published). As we have seen, the change of sign is important for its bearing on the applicability of the Lennard-Jones model. Theoretical values of the thermal diffusion factor for the $(13, 7)$ case have been calculated for one of the mixtures in which reversal occurs—nitrogen-argon—following the procedure described above (§5.4). These are shown together with Waldmann's experimental values in fig. 32, where it appears that the reversal of sign actually occurs at a temperature about $25°$ above the theoretical value. The $(13, 7)$ case is therefore not wholly satisfactory, but the discrepancy is small enough to suggest that, with somewhat different indices, a Lennard-Jones model could represent closely the observed behaviour of this mixture.

TABLE X. *The thermal diffusion factor at various temperatures* (*Waldmann,* 1949)

	$T°K.$ ...	89	194	283	372
	H_2-N_2				
	$n_{10} = 0.1$	0.14	—	0.42	—
	$n_{10} = 0.9$	0.08	0.17	0.21	0.22
	N_2-A	-0.031	0.044	0.070	—
	O_2-A	-0.037	0.026	0.050	—
Values of α	N_2-O_2	$|\alpha| < 0.001$	0.012	0.017	—
	N_2-CO_2	—	-0.006	0.036	0.051
	O_2-CO_2	—	0.006	0.036	0.046
	A-CO_2	—	0.026	0.019	0.014
	C_2H_4-N_2	—	-0.018	-0.014	-0.013
	C_2H_4-O_2	—	-0.013	-0.005	0.001
	C_2H_4-A	—	-0.007	0.027	0.041

CHAPTER VII

APPLICATION OF THERMAL DIFFUSION TO THE SEPARATION OF GAS MIXTURES

The earlier experimental work on thermal diffusion was directed chiefly to the elucidation of the nature of molecular interactions. That thermal diffusion was of immediate practical importance was first shown in 1938, when Clusius and Dickel announced that they had applied thermal diffusion to effect a partial separation of the isotopes of chlorine. In the following year they published the results of further work in which these isotopes had been almost completely separated. A considerable stimulus was thus given to the study of thermal diffusion in all its aspects.

7.1. The method of Clusius and Dickel

The apparatus used by Clusius and Dickel (1939) is simple. It consists of a long vertical tube, along the axis of which is a wire which can be heated electrically; the tube itself is cooled by a stream of water over its outer surface. A gas mixture in the tube is thus subjected to a transverse temperature gradient. The gradient produces two effects: first, thermal diffusion in the direction of the gradient, and secondly, a convective motion of the gas upwards near the hot wire and downwards near the cold wall. As a result of this convection the separating effect of thermal diffusion is made cumulative.

How this comes about can be understood as follows. We imagine a gas mixture, for example, hydrogen-nitrogen, in an enclosure of rectangular section, the longer sides of which are vertical and at different temperatures. Thermal diffusion causes the heavier (nitrogen) molecules to move towards the cold wall, where because of convection they are carried downwards; the lighter (hydrogen) molecules diffuse towards the hot wall and are carried upwards. We assume that the gas can be divided into two streams, in each of which the velocity is constant over the cross-section. Let the two streams be divided into equal volume elements, in each of which the composition can be considered uniform, as indicated in fig. 33*a*, and suppose that diffusion and convection take place, not simultaneously, but alternately, the time for diffusion being such that concentration equilibrium is reached, and for convection such that the gas in one element moves into the neighbouring element. Then

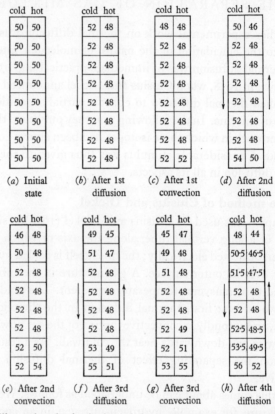

Fig. 33. Illustrating the beginning of the course of concentration changes in a column in which convection and thermal diffusion are supposed to occur alternately. The figures denote the concentration of the heavier component; the separation due to thermal diffusion alone is assumed to be 4 % throughout.

the course of the changes in composition which occur as diffusion is succeeded by convection is shown in fig. 33 *b–h*, where it has been assumed that the initial composition of the mixture is 50 % and the separation due to thermal diffusion alone is 4 % and independent of composition. With hydrogen-nitrogen a separation of this amount would be produced if the mean temperatures of the two streams were 300 and 500° K. This simplified picture makes clear how, after the initial stages, a given element of gas is continually brought by convection into juxtaposition with another element with which it is not in equilibrium. The result is that there is an accumulation of the heavier molecules at the bottom of the enclosure and of the lighter at the top, the difference in composition between the top and bottom elements being much greater than that effected by thermal diffusion alone. The final state attained is one in which the separating effect of thermal diffusion is balanced by the remixing brought about by convection and by concentration diffusion in the vertical direction.

Using a tube 1 m. in length and 1 cm. in diameter, with the wire heated to about 500° C., Clusius and Dickel showed that a hydrogen-carbon dioxide mixture could be almost completely separated, in the sense that the gas at the extremities of the column consisted of the almost pure components. They were able with this mixture to demonstrate visually the existence of the longitudinal concentration gradient, for by suitably adjusting the current in the heating wire the upper part of the wire could be made to appear dark while the lower part glowed brightly. This was due of course to the thermal conductivity of the hydrogen at the top of the column being greater than that of the carbon dioxide at the bottom.

With a column of similar construction, but 2·6 m. in length, a partial separation of the neon isotopes was effected. The analysis, made by means of a mass spectrometer, showed that after operating the column for a few days, samples of neon could be obtained containing 31 % of the heaviest isotope, ^{22}Ne, instead of the normal 9·7 %, and 0·6 % of the intermediate isotope, ^{21}Ne, instead of the normal 0·3 %. Clusius and Dickel then investigated the action of the column, studying the effect of variation of wire temperature, of dimensions, and of pressure of the gas mixture. They pointed out the possibility of using batteries of columns coupled together convectively and so of effectively increasing the length, and they referred also to the possible applications of the method to the purification of gases, to the separation of liquid mixtures, and the deposition of mists and smokes.

After this preliminary work an attempt was made to separate the chlorine isotopes. For this purpose five columns were used in series giving a total length of 36 m. The chlorine was used in the form of hydrogen chloride. Samples taken after a few days from the top of the first column and bottom of the last showed on analysis by density determination that an almost complete separation had been effected. The best result was 96 % $H^{35}Cl$ at top and 99·4 % $H^{37}Cl$ at bottom. With neon, 2·5 l. of gas were prepared containing 99·7 % ^{22}Ne at a rate equivalent to 300 cm.^{3} per week.

7.2. The theory of the column

The theory of the separating column was first discussed by Clusius and Dickel (1939), and later by Waldmann (1939) and by van der Grinten (1939), all of whom treated the gas mixture as contained between plane surfaces instead of, as is usual in practice, cylindrical ones. A further simplification was made in that the density, thermal conductivity, viscosity and diffusivity of the gas were regarded as independent of temperature. A more rigorous treatment was given by Furry, Jones and Onsager (1939), who obtained a general solution in terms of certain integrals for any fluid, and particular solutions in the two cases of a gas whose molecules are Maxwellian and rigid spheres. The cylindrical case was considered by Furry and Jones (1946). A further development of the theory was made by Bardeen (1940). The theory is mathematically rather complex, and consequently Clark Jones and Furry (1946) have given an elementary theory which brings out more clearly than the rigorous treatment the physical processes in the column and which leads to results differing from those obtained rigorously only by numerical factors. An account of this elementary theory follows.

The problem is considered in two parts. The first is the purely hydrodynamical one of the convective flow in the column, the second is the determination of the net transport of each component of the mixture up the column. The following simplifying assumptions are made:

(i) The two components have molecular masses which are so little different that the variation of density with composition of the mixture may be ignored.

(ii) The temperature dependence of the viscosity, conductivity and diffusivity can be neglected. Except in deriving the convection velocity the temperature dependence of the density is also negligible.

(iii) The gas mixture is contained between plane walls and moves in two streams, one up, one down, the column, the velocity being uniform over the cross-section of each stream.

(iv) The flow is lamellar.

(v) The temperature distribution is that determined by conduction alone.

The direction of the normal to the wall is taken as the x-axis; the distance between the walls being $2w$, the range of x is from $-w$ to $+w$. The width of the walls is b, in the y direction, and the height is L, in the z direction. The temperatures of the walls are T' and T; $T' - T = \Delta T$ and $(T' + T)/2 = \bar{T}$.

Determination of the convection velocity. The equation for the steady flow of an element of fluid contained between the walls is

$$\eta \frac{d^2v}{dx^2} - \rho g - \frac{dp}{dz} = 0, \tag{7.1}$$

where η is the viscosity, v is the velocity in the z direction, ρ is the density and p the pressure. Here the pressure gradient dp/dz is equal to $-\bar{\rho}g$, where $\bar{\rho}$ is the mean density over the cross-section, hence

$$\eta \frac{d^2v}{dx^2} = (\rho - \bar{\rho})g.$$

The density ρ can be expressed approximately as a linear function of the mean density $\bar{\rho}$ thus:

$$\rho = \bar{\rho}\left(1 - \frac{T - \bar{T}}{\bar{T}}\right).$$

Since from assumption (ii) the thermal conductivity is independent of temperature, and the temperature gradient is therefore uniform,

$$T = \bar{T} + \frac{x}{2w}\Delta T.$$

Thus

$$\rho = \bar{\rho}\left(1 - \frac{x}{2w}\frac{\Delta T}{\bar{T}}\right)$$

and

$$\eta \frac{d^2v}{dx^2} = -\rho g \frac{x}{2w}\frac{\Delta T}{\bar{T}},$$

ignoring the distinction between ρ and $\bar{\rho}$. Integration gives

$$v = \frac{\rho g}{12\eta}\frac{\Delta T}{w\bar{T}}x(w^2 - x^2), \tag{7.2}$$

where the fact that $v = 0$ for $x = \pm w$ has been used. The velocity thus varies over the cross-section as shown in fig. 34. The mean speed over the range $x = 0$ to w is

$$\bar{v} = \frac{\rho g}{48\eta} \frac{\Delta T}{T} w^2, \tag{7.3}$$

and this is the velocity which must be attributed to each of the two streams when the velocity is regarded as uniform over the cross-section of each.

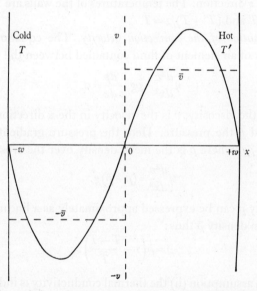

Fig. 34. The variation of convection velocity v with distance from the walls ($x = 0$ is the mid-plane between the walls). In the simple treatment given the gas is regarded as moving in two streams each with uniform velocity $\bar{v}$. (After Clark Jones and Furry, 1946.)

Determination of the transport. The flow of molecules of either species up the column is determined by two factors—the convection current and the process of concentration diffusion which comes into play as soon as a longitudinal concentration gradient is established. Because of thermal diffusion the concentration of the heavier molecules (1) in the upward moving stream is less than that in the downward stream. Let the number density in the upward stream, averaged over the cross-section, be n_1'' and in the downward stream

n_1'; then the transport of molecules (1) down the column due to the convection currents, of mean speed $\bar{v}$, is

$$(n_1' - n_1'')\,\bar{v}wb,$$

and due to concentration diffusion

$$nD_{12}\frac{dn_{10}}{dz}\,2wb,$$

where n and n_{10} are mean values of the total number density of both species, and the relative density of the species (1) respectively. The net number transport down the column is therefore

$$(n_1' - n_1'')\,\bar{v}wb + nD_{12}\frac{dn_{10}}{dz}\,2wb,$$

or $\qquad n(n_{10}' - n_{10}'')\,\bar{v}wb + nD_{12}\frac{dn_{10}}{dz}\,2wb,$

disregarding the variation of n with temperature. The mass of molecules transported is

$$\tau_1 = \rho(n_{10}' - n_{10}'')\,\bar{v}wb + \rho D_{12}\frac{dn_{10}}{dz}\,2wb. \qquad (7\cdot4)$$

Jones and Furry now make the assumption that the time rate of change of concentration at any point is small, so that in effect conditions are steady. This condition is fulfilled if at each end of the column there is a reservoir large compared with the volume of the column itself. In this quasi-steady state the factors tending to change $(n_{10}' - n_{10}'')$ must have a zero resultant. These factors are convection and diffusion. It can be seen from fig. 33 that the effect of convection is to reduce the difference in concentration $(n_{10}' - n_{10}'')$ which exists at any value of z in the column, for two juxtaposed elements of the fluid are replaced by others of smaller difference. The relative motion of the two streams causes n_1' to decrease by $-\bar{v}\dfrac{dn_1}{dz}$ per second, and n_1'' to increase by the same amount; hence the net rate of decrease of $(n_{10}' - n_{10}'')$ due to convection is $-2\bar{v}\dfrac{dn_1}{dz}$. Thermal diffusion transverse to the flow tends to increase the concentration difference. The number flux density of molecules (1) due to thermal diffusion is

$$\Gamma_1 = -nD_{12}\left[\frac{dn_{10}}{dx} + k_T\frac{1}{T}\frac{dT}{dx}\right].$$

Since this flux is into a layer of gas of thickness w, n_1' increases at the rate Γ_1/w, and n_1'' decreases at the same rate, hence $(n_1' - n_1'')$ increases at the rate $2\Gamma_1/w$. In the quasi-steady state therefore

$$\frac{2\Gamma_1}{w} + 2\bar{v}\frac{dn_1}{dz} = 0.$$

If in the expression for Γ_1 we write

$$\frac{dn_{10}}{dx} = \frac{n_{10}' - n_{10}''}{w}, \quad \frac{dT}{dx} = -\frac{\Delta T}{2w} \quad \text{and} \quad k_T = \alpha n_{10} n_{20},$$

we now find

$$n_{10}' - n_{10}'' = \alpha n_{10} n_{20} \frac{\Delta T}{2\bar{T}} + \frac{w^2 \bar{v}}{D_{12}} \frac{dn_{10}}{dz},$$

and substitution of this in the expression for the mass flux gives

$$\tau_1 = \rho \bar{v} w b \left[\alpha n_{10} n_{20} \frac{\Delta T}{2\bar{T}} + \frac{w^2 v}{D_{12}} \frac{dn_{10}}{dz} \right] + \rho D_{12} \frac{dn_{10}}{dz} 2wb$$

$$= H n_{10} n_{20} + (K_c + K_d) \frac{dn_{10}}{dz}, \tag{7.5}$$

where
$$H = \frac{\alpha \rho^2 g w^3 b}{96\eta} \left(\frac{\Delta T}{\bar{T}}\right)^2, \quad K_c = \frac{\rho^3 g^2 w^7 b}{48^2 \eta^2 D_{12}} \left(\frac{\Delta T}{\bar{T}}\right)^2; \left.\right\} \tag{7.6}$$

and
$$K_d = \rho D_{12} . 2wb.$$

The three terms represent respectively the contributions of thermal diffusion, convection and longitudinal diffusion. The more exact theory, which takes account of the temperature dependence of density, conductivity, etc., and the variation of convection velocity over the cross-section, leads to a similar expression for the transport but with different numerical factors in H and K_c. There is also to be added to $(K_c + K_d)$ a term, K_p, representing the remixing effect of small irregularities in dimensions and temperature distribution in the column. This term cannot be estimated theoretically but it can be determined experimentally.

The steady state. If the processes of convection and diffusion continue, a steady state will ultimately be reached in which the transport is zero. Then

$$H n_{10} n_{20} = -K \frac{dn_{10}}{dz}, \quad \text{where} \quad K = K_c + K_d + K_p,$$

from which we have

$$\ln (n_{10}/n_{20}) = -\frac{H}{K} dz + \text{constant},$$

or

$$\ln \frac{(n_{10}/n_{20})_l}{(n_{10}/n_{20})_u} = \frac{H}{K}(z_u - z_l) = \frac{H}{K}L, \qquad (7.7)$$

where subscripts u and l refer to upper and lower ends of the column and L is the length of the column. Hence

$$q_e = e^{2AL}, \qquad (7.8)$$

where q_e is the separation factor (cf. p. 37) and $A = H/2K$. For the production of a large separation, therefore, the column must be long and the ratio of the thermal diffusion effect, as represented by H, to the remixing effect, measured by K, should be large. It may readily be shown that A, regarded as a function of the spacing $2w$ of the walls has a maximum value when $K_d = 2K_c$, that is, when

$$w = \left(\frac{\eta D}{\rho g}\right)^{\frac{1}{3}} 48^{\frac{1}{3}} \left(\frac{\Delta T}{T}\right)^{-\frac{1}{3}}.$$

This maximum value of A is

$$A_{\max} = \frac{8\alpha}{48^{\frac{4}{3}}} \left(\frac{\rho g}{\eta D}\right)^{\frac{1}{3}} \left(\frac{\Delta T}{\bar{T}}\right)^{\frac{4}{3}}.$$

(The exact theory gives a numerical factor $105^{\frac{4}{3}}/180$.) The value of the spacing which gives the maximum separation factor can therefore be calculated for given temperatures T and T'. In the more rigorous theory, the variation of the convection velocity in the x direction is taken into account, and so also is the temperature dependence of the viscosity, etc., of the gas. A knowledge of the nature of the molecular interactions is, however, required for this, and the theoretical expressions are based on the assumption that the molecules are either Maxwellian or rigid spheres. Some divergence between the theoretical and experimental results is therefore to be expected.

In so far as comparison is possible the theory is in general confirmed. The most exacting test, according to Jones and Furry, is that concerned with the effect of pressure on the equilibrium separation factor q_e. The theory gives

$$\ln q_e = \frac{HL}{K_c + K_d + K_p}.$$

The expressions for H and K show that if p is the pressure, $H \propto p^2$, $K_c \propto p^4$, K_d is independent of p, and $K_p \propto p^4$ (since $n \propto p$, $\rho \propto p$, $D_{12} \propto p^{-1}$, and K_p must vary in the same way as K_c). Hence

$$\ln q_e = \frac{a/p^2}{1 + b/p^4},$$

where the quantities a and b cannot be evaluated theoretically because of the unknown quantity K_p associated with 'parasitic' convection currents. There is clearly an optimum working pressure, for q_e has a maximum value when $p = b^{\frac{1}{4}}$. As will be seen below, experiment confirms this relation between q_e and p, and it therefore seems likely that the theory is substantially correct.

7.3. Modes of operation and the efficiency of columns

A separating column is usually required to produce with greatest economy of materials and energy a supply of gas mixture enriched in one of its components. For this purpose a column may be used in one of two ways. In discontinuous operation the mixture is allowed to separate for a time long enough for the state to become nearly steady and then the gas at either end of the column is withdrawn. In continuous operation gas is removed at a small constant rate from the column, so that the maximum separation is never attained. Jones and Furry have considered these two modes of operation and have given expressions for the final concentrations which may be obtained for a specified rate of withdrawal in continuous operation, and for the rate of approach to equilibrium for columns operated discontinuously.

The problem of obtaining maximum efficiency falls into two parts. First there is the determination of the best values of H and K, that is, of the temperatures T and T' and wall spacing $2w$. The properties of the gas mixture are here involved. Then when H and K are fixed, there is the determination of the best length of column to use, for the same amount of enriched gas mixture can be obtained from a shorter column operated near the steady state as from a longer column operated farther from the steady state. The precise conditions for maximum efficiency are not easily formulated, but Jones and Furry give two guiding principles. The first is that the spacing $2w$ should be adjusted so that K_c/K_d has a value between 5 and 25;

this leads to optimum values for H and K, and ensures that the flow is always lamellar. Secondly, the rate of withdrawal of gas should be such that the separation factor obtaining in the column is equal to the square root of the equilibrium separation factor q_e. From these principles one can calculate the dimensions required for the production at a given rate of a mixture enriched to a given amount in one of its components when the initial composition is known. By using a number of columns in series-parallel arrangement the conditions for maximum efficiency can be satisfied over each section instead of over the column as a whole. Furry and Jones have given examples of the design of such a multi-stage apparatus for certain gas mixtures.

7.4. Experimental work

Two types of column are commonly used. In the first the gas mixture is confined in the space between two coaxial tubes of glass or metal, maintained at different temperatures. This is referred to as the coaxial tube type. In the other, the hot-wire type, the gas is contained in a tube down the axis of which is a wire which can be heated electrically. This type can be regarded as an extreme case of the coaxial tube. Both types may have reservoirs at one or both ends. The dimensions of the tubes should be suited to the gas mixture which is to be treated, optimum values being calculable from the theory, as will be seen later. In the coaxial tube type, the inner tube usually has a radius of 1–2 cm., and the outer about 1 cm. more; the length of a unit is usually restricted by the available space to a few metres, though several units may be coupled together to give a greater effective length.

The hot-wire type has the advantage over the coaxial tube of simpler construction. Also, it permits larger temperature gradients to be used, and the energy loss by radiation is smaller. A disadvantage is that the wire may be attacked by one of the components of the mixture. If the temperature difference which can be used is small, because, for example, of the possibility of chemical decomposition, then the coaxial tube type is preferable, since larger values of the separation factor can be obtained with it than with the hot-wire type operating at the same temperatures. In multi-stage apparatus it may be advantageous to use both types.

To illustrate the construction and behaviour of the column some typical experimental work will now be reviewed, more particularly that which bears on the theory of the column.

Separation of isotopic methane. Nier (1940*a*) used a column of the coaxial tube type to concentrate $^{13}CH_4$. The characteristics of the column were:

	Hot wall	Cold wall
Material	Steel	Brass
Radius (cm.)	1·74	2·46
Temp. (°K.)	573	300
Length (m.)		7·30
Power (W./m.)		377

The inner tube was heated by means of a nichrome wire which passed down the axis and which was separated from the tube by porcelain insulators. Its temperature was determined from the expansion. The outer wall was cooled by water which flowed at such a rate that the difference of the inlet and outlet temperatures was about 5° C.

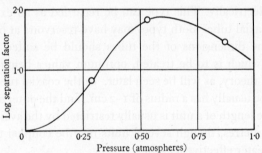

Fig. 35. The dependence of the separation factor on pressure.
(After Nier, 1940*a*.)

In studying its operation, the column was used without reservoirs. It was filled with methane containing the isotopes ^{12}C and ^{13}C in the natural proportions, and at intervals samples were withdrawn for analysis by mass spectrometer. The rate at which the equilibrium state was approached could therefore be determined and the equilibrium separation factor q_e found by extrapolation. This was done for various values of the pressure. The results are shown graphically in fig. 35. Nier, and later Furry and Jones (1946), compared these experimental results with the theory. It is clear that there is agreement in so far as the experimental values of q_e have a maximum. Further, the dependence of q_e on pressure p can be expressed by the relation

$$\ln q_e = \frac{1 \cdot 72/p^2}{1 \cdot 283 + 0 \cdot 162/p^4}.$$

Using the known values from the density, viscosity, etc., of methane and the dimensions of the column to calculate H and K, Jones and Furry find

$$\ln q_e = \frac{1 \cdot 710/p^2}{1 + 0 \cdot 163/p^4}.$$

The theoretical and experimental values are thus in good agreement —better, in fact, than is to be expected from the accuracy with which the quantities used in deriving the theoretical value are known. The difference in the purely numerical term is a measure of the effect of 'parasitic' remixing which is not allowed for in evaluating q_e theoretically. Nier's measurements of the rate of approach to equilibrium have been discussed by Bardeen (1940), who finds them in satisfactory agreement with the theory.

Concentration of ^{3}He. McInteer, Aldrich and Nier (1947, 1948) have used a three-stage apparatus to concentrate the isotope ^{3}He. The natural abundance of this in the original well-helium used is only $1 \cdot 5 \times 10^{-5} \%$. The design of the columns was similar to that proposed by Jones and Furry (1946). The first two stages were of the coaxial tube type and the third stage a hot-wire column. The details were as follows:

Column no.	1		2		3	
	Hot wall	Cold wall	Hot wall	Cold wall	Hot wall	Cold wall
Material	Steel	Brass	Steel	Brass	Platinum	Brass
Radius (cm.)	3·02	3·65	1·75	2·38	0·018	0·466
Temp. (°K.)	600	300	600	300	1100	300
Length (m.)	3·5		3·5		2·54	
Power (W./m.)	2860		1430		630	

For the production of large quantities of enriched gas the columns were joined in series. The first two columns were connected by a short length of wide-bore tubing, and the second and third by a length of copper tubing in which a forced convection was maintained. Traces of hydrogen were removed by means of palladium thimbles at the upper ends of the last two columns. In this way the columns yielded, at the rate of 14 cm.^{3} per day, gas containing $0\cdot21\,\%$ of ^{3}He.

In investigating the behaviour of the columns, the coupling between the second and third stages was broken, and the hot-wire column and the coupled coaxial tube columns were then examined separately. The difference in the cross-sections of the coaxial tube columns was justifiably disregarded in evaluating the theoretical quantities.

The columns were first operated continuously, with a flow of normal helium maintained across the lower end and an outward flow σ of gas enriched in ^{3}He from the upper. For this case Jones and Furry give for the separation factor

$$q = \frac{1+\nu}{e^{-2AL(1+\nu)}+\nu}, \quad \text{where} \quad \nu = \sigma/H,$$

or when $\nu \ll 1$ and $2AL$ is large, as was the case experimentally,

$$q = H/\sigma.$$

Thus an experimental value of H could be determined from the measured separation factor and the known rate of withdrawal of gas, σ. This was compared with the theoretical value of H calculated from the dimensions of the column and the properties of the gas, with the results shown below:

Column	Press. (atm.)	σ (std. litres per day)	q	H (exp.)	H (th.)
1 and 2 in series	7·8	0·667	386	257	266
3	7·8	0·050	330	16·5	9·5
	9·7	0·080	310	24·8	14·8

Next, the columns were operated discontinuously, that is, no gas was withdrawn. The separation factor obtaining at time t was measured; from it the quantity $A = H/2K$ could be calculated, for Jones and Furry give for these experimental conditions

$$q - 1 = Ht\,2A/\mu,$$

where μ is the mass of gas per unit length of column. This experimental value of A is compared with the theoretical value below.

Column	Pressure (atm.)	$2A$ (exp.)	$2A$ (th.)
1 and 2 in series	7·8	0·017	0·020
	9·7	0·012	0·014
3	7·8	0·023	0·052
	9·7	0·019	0·062

Here, as in the previous comparison of H values, the agreement is reasonably good for the coaxial tube columns (1 and 2) but poor for the hot-wire column. The lack of agreement in this case is probably due to the fact that the values of the density, viscosity, etc., of the gas are calculated for a mean temperature $\bar{T} = \frac{1}{2}(T + T')$; this mean is clearly less suitable for a hot-wire column than for a coaxial tube. Simon (1946) has found similar results when a hot-wire column was used for the separation of the argon isotopes; he has shown, however, that the choice of a more reasonable average value of the temperature leads to better agreement.

Concentration of $^{18}O_2$. This has been several times carried out. Clusius and Dickel (1944) have used a hot-wire apparatus consisting of six stages of total length 82 m. The wire was a platinum alloy, 0·4 mm. in diameter, heated to a temperature of 700° C.; the surrounding glass tube had a mean diameter of about 18 mm. in the first four stages and less in the last two. With this Clusius and Dickel obtained gas containing 90 % $^{18}O_2$ and 10 % $^{17}O^{18}O$. Further treatment in another column led to the production of 250 cm.³ of gas in which the proportions were 99 % $^{18}O_2$ and 1 % $^{17}O^{18}O$. Lauder (1947) and Whalley, Winter and Briscoe (1949) also have concentrated this isotope. Although the degree of concentration achieved is relatively small—21·9 % $^{18}O_2$—Whalley and Winter (1949) investigated the performance of their column, which was of the coaxial tube type, 10 m. long, and compared their results with the theory. The theoretical variation of the equilibrium separation factor with pressure was again confirmed.

Among other separations effected to a greater or less extent by means of the column are those of the isotopes of krypton and xenon

by Groth and Harteck (1940) and Clusius and Dickel (1940) and
by Clusius (1949); of nitrogen by Clusius and Becker (1947); and
of mercury by Groth and Harteck (1939). Schäfer and Corte (1946)
have used the column to demonstrate the possibility (which depends
on a quantum mechanical effect) of separating *ortho*- and *para*-
hydrogen.

Although the theory of the column as developed by Furry, Jones
and Onsager appears to be correct in general, it is not yet sufficiently
precise to enable experimental measurements of the separation
obtained with a column to be applied to the determination of the
thermal diffusion factor. Such a procedure would be useful in
the case of those mixtures which in the static—non-convective—
diffusion experiment yield a separation too small to be accurately
measured. The column is, however, a valuable means of determining
the sign of the thermal diffusion factor (cf. §5.1).

CHAPTER VIII

THERMAL DIFFUSION IN LIQUIDS: THE SORET EFFECT

8.1. Introduction

It was in a solution that the phenomenon of thermal diffusion was first observed. Ludwig in 1856 described an experiment in which an aqueous solution of sodium sulphate was contained in an inverted U-tube, one limb of which was heated in boiling water and the other cooled in ice. After a few days the concentration of the salt in the cool limb was found to exceed that in the hot one. This effect was rediscovered and examined more fully by Soret, whose name has since been given to it. In papers published in 1879–81 Soret describes experiments which led him to conclude that when two parts of one and the same salt solution are maintained at different temperatures a diffusion process occurs which increases the concentration of the salt in the colder part at the expense of the warmer. His apparatus consisted of a straight tube, about 30 cm. long and 2 cm. wide, mounted vertically. It was heated at the upper end and cooled at the lower, the temperature gradient being maintained for times as long as 55 days, after which samples were withdrawn for analysis. Some typical results are given in Table XI; they relate to a solution of potassium chloride in water. The concentrations, even in the long time allowed, did not reach their equilibrium values, as Soret himself observed.

As a result of these and other measurements with solutions of sodium and lithium chlorides, potassium nitrate and copper sulphate, Soret concluded that:

(i) in all cases the concentration of the solute increases in the colder part;

(ii) the separation $(c - c')$ increases with the initial concentration —for sodium and potassium chlorides nearly proportionally;

(iii) for the alkali chlorides the separation is greater the greater the molecular weight.

A theoretical explanation of the effect was suggested by van't Hoff (1887) who pointed out that the direction of the concentration

TABLE XI. *Thermal diffusion in* KCl *solutions* (Soret)

c	c'	$(c-c')/c$
24·885	23·191	0·0680
17·937	16·712	0·0684
12·522	11·846	0·0541
10·540	9·827	0·0679

c, mass of salt per 100 g. of solution in cold region at temperature $T = 20°$ C.
c', the same in warm region at temperature $T' = 80°$ C.

gradient set up was that to be expected if the solute distributes itself so as to give a uniform osmotic pressure. If P represents the osmotic pressure and c the concentration of the solute then $P = cRT$, and if in the steady state P is constant, then cT is constant throughout the solution. Thus the concentration of the solute should be greater in the colder region, as is found. Quantitatively, however, the theory was soon shown to be untenable. Several attempts have since been made to give a satisfactory theoretical explanation. An interesting thermodynamical approach is based on the application of the work of Meixner and Onsager on the thermodynamics of irreversible processes; this is discussed by de Groot (1945). It leads to a relation between the Soret coefficient (which is analogous to the thermal diffusion factor α of the gas theory) and a thermodynamic quantity—the heat of transport—which, however, itself requires definition in terms of kinetic theory concepts. Chapman in 1929, having in mind the complexity of the theory of thermal diffusion in gases, expressed the opinion that the prospect of arriving at even an approximate kinetic theory of the effect in liquids was remote. The developments in the theory of the liquid state made by Born and Green (1946, 1947) have brought the prospect nearer. In a recent paper Yang (1949) has extended Born and Green's theory to liquid mixtures and has derived the equation of diffusion. Thus far, however, the coefficients are found in general terms only. For a discussion of the theoretical aspects of the Soret effect, reference must be made to the monograph by de Groot.

8.2. The equation of diffusion and the Soret coefficient

Experimental results relating to thermal diffusion in liquids are usually expressed in terms of the Soret coefficient σ. This coefficient is formally comparable with (α/T), where α is the thermal diffusion factor of the preceding theory of the effect in gases.

In dealing with diffusion in solutions it is usually assumed that, in analogy with the case of a gas mixture, the flux density of the solute or solvent can be expressed as the sum of two components, one due to the concentration gradient, the other due to the temperature gradient (cf. 2.4). Thus the flux density of the solute across a surface at rest with respect to the solution is taken as

$$\mathbf{\Gamma}_1 = -\nu \left[D \frac{\partial \nu_{10}}{\partial \mathbf{r}} + D' \nu_{10} \nu_{20} \frac{\partial T}{\partial \mathbf{r}} \right], \qquad (8.1)$$

where $\mathbf{\Gamma}_1 =$ the flux density in moles per unit area per unit time,

$\nu =$ the total number of moles (of solute and solvent) per unit volume,

$\nu_{10}, \nu_{20} =$ the molar fractions of solute and solvent respectively,

$D =$ the coefficient of concentration diffusion

and $\quad D' =$ the coefficient of thermal diffusion.

By treating the solution as if it comprises only two species of particle, and using molar quantities instead of molecular quantities, the coefficients D and D' are defined in such a way that they can be determined experimentally. But most solutions—clearly so when they are electrolytes—ought, from the point of view of a kinetic theory, to be treated as multicomponent systems; the theoretical significance of the experimentally determined coefficients D and D' will therefore be even more difficult to state than that of the corresponding coefficients in the case of gas mixtures.

The postulated equation of diffusion can be written

$$\mathbf{\Gamma}_1 = -\nu D \left[\frac{\partial \nu_{10}}{\partial \mathbf{r}} + \frac{D'}{D} \nu_{10} \nu_{20} \frac{\partial T}{\partial \mathbf{r}} \right],$$

or with $\sigma = D'/D$,

$$\mathbf{\Gamma}_1 = -\nu D \left[\frac{\partial \nu_{10}}{\partial \mathbf{r}} + \sigma \nu_{10} \nu_{20} \frac{\partial T}{\partial \mathbf{r}} \right], \qquad (8.2)$$

where σ is called the Soret coefficient. There is therefore a formal correspondence between σ and α/T, as comparison with (2.4) shows.

In the steady state the flux vanishes, and

$$\sigma = -\frac{1}{v_{10}v_{20}}\frac{dv_{10}}{dT},$$

or

$$\sigma = \frac{1}{(T'-T)}\ln\frac{(v_{10}/v_{20})}{(v'_{10}/v'_{20})} = \frac{\ln q}{(T'-T)}, \tag{8.3}$$

where v'_{10}, v'_{20} refer to the region at temperature T' and v_{10}, v_{20} to the region at temperature $T < T'$, and q is the separation factor. It is here assumed that σ can be regarded as constant in the range of integration. For dilute solutions $v_{20} \to 1$ and then

$$\sigma = -\frac{1}{v_{10}}\frac{dv_{10}}{dT} = \frac{\ln(v_{10}/v'_{10})}{T'-T}. \tag{8.4}$$

The quantity determined experimentally is usually the difference in molality of the solution in two regions at temperatures T and T'. If this difference in molality is $(v'_1 - v_1) = \Delta v_1$ and $(T' - T) = \Delta T$, then the fractional difference per degree is $\dfrac{1}{v_1}\dfrac{\Delta v_1}{\Delta T}$, where v_1 is the initial uniform molality. In terms of this quantity the Soret coefficient as it has been defined above is given approximately by

$$\sigma = -\frac{1}{1-\rho_1/\rho}\frac{1}{v_1}\frac{\Delta v_1}{\Delta T}, \tag{8.5}$$

where $\rho_1 =$ mass of solute per unit volume of solution and $\rho =$ density of solution. Thus for dilute solutions σ is equal to the fractional change in molality per degree, and indeed some workers take this as the definition of the Soret coefficient. For any but dilute solutions, however, the first factor is important.

8.3. Experimental methods and results

Of the solutions for which the Soret effect has been measured the majority are aqueous electrolytes; there are results for a few non-electrolytes and non-aqueous solutions and for some metallic solutions. A survey shows at once that the results of different workers are more frequently than not discordant—an indication of the difficulties attending the measurement of this effect.

One such difficulty is due to the long time normally required for the steady state to be attained. De Groot has deduced from the postulated expression for the flux that the approach to the steady state is exponential. For diffusion in a solution contained between parallel plates separated by a distance a (small compared with the plate dimensions), he finds that the time for the concentration to reach to within $1/e$th of the final value is

$$\tau = \frac{a^2}{\pi^2 D}.$$

For many aqueous solutions D is of the order of 0·5 cm.²/day, so that for $a = 10$ cm., $\tau = 20$ days, and for the composition to reach to within 1 % of the final value a time of 5τ or 100 days must be allowed. It is clearly advantageous to reduce the dimensions of the diffusion apparatus as far as possible.

With this aim Wereide (1914) used a diffusion vessel consisting of a glass cylinder only 15 mm. in height. The cylinder was closed by metal reservoirs through which water was circulated from supplies at different temperatures. The time required for the steady state to be reached was in most cases 2 or 3 days. The changes in composition of the solution in the cylinder were determined from the refractivities of samples of solution drawn by pipette from the upper, warmer, part and from the lower, colder, part.

A more extensive series of measurements with a somewhat similar apparatus was made by Tanner (1927). Here the solution filled a shallow cell only 10 mm. deep, bounded top and bottom by the silver-plated surfaces of two hollow copper blocks and at the sides by four strips of optically plane glass. The copper blocks were kept at constant but different temperatures by circulating water; in most cases the temperatures were 38 and 24° C. With this small cell the steady state was reached for some solutions in 10 hr. or less, and in most cases within 24 hr. The concentration gradient in the cell was determined optically. Parallel light was passed through a slit which was inclined to the horizontal. It then passed through the solution and was focused by a cylindrical lens on a photographic plate. With a solution uniform in composition and temperature the image of the slit was horizontal. When a temperature gradient was set up in the solution the resulting gradient of refractive index caused the image to be displaced and inclined to the horizontal. From the mean displacement the difference in refractive index of the upper and lower layers of the solution could be deduced. This difference was the sum of two effects—the temperature variation of refractive index with temperature and the variation due to the concentration gradient set up by thermal diffusion. The contributions of these two effects could be determined separately, since the temperature gradient became steady in a few minutes after passing warm water through the upper block, and in this short time no appreciable

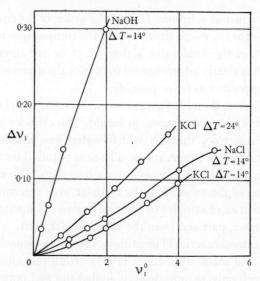

Fig. 36. The difference in molality $\Delta \nu_1$ for various initial concentrations, ν_1^0. (Values from Tanner, 1927.)

change in composition occurred. To find the concentration gradient from the difference in refractive index, the rate of change of refractive index with concentration was required. This was determined with a refractometer.

Tanner measured the difference in molality $\Delta \nu_1$ set up by thermal diffusion in numerous solutions at various concentrations and in some cases with different temperature gradients. Some of his results are shown graphically. In fig. 36 the difference in molality $\Delta \nu_1$ is shown as a function of the initial concentration ν_1^0 for solutions of KCl, NaCl and NaOH. The first two were examined with two temperature gradients: in the first T was about 25° C., T' about 49° C., giving $\Delta T = 24$° C.; and in the second T was again 25° C., but T' was $39°$ C., giving a difference $\Delta T = 14°$ C. The effect of the different gradients is shown in fig. 37, which refers to KCl solutions. The increase in $\Delta \nu_1$ with increasing concentration in these solutions appears to be general, though for HCl, H_2SO_4 and KOH solutions, which were examined at concentrations as high as 8 molar, $\Delta \nu_1$ reaches a maximum value and then decreases. In figs. 38 and 39 the values of the Soret coefficient σ, calculated from the expression (8.5) are shown. It will be observed that the non-electrolyte—cane sugar—has a value of σ of the same order as that for electrolytes.

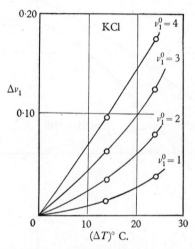

Fig. 37. The difference in molality due to different temperature gradients. (Values from Tanner, 1927.)

Chipman (1926) also studied the Soret effect in a large number of solutions. He used a conductivity method of analysis when the solution was a dilute electrolyte, and for other solutions titration or optical methods. His conductivity cell was provided with two pairs of electrodes, one at each end. Its length was about 14 cm. and diameter about 3·5 cm. The cell was mounted with its upper part in one thermostat, its lower in another. The temperatures of the two baths differed by only 10° C., the values being 20 and 30° C. or sometimes 25 and 35° C.; these temperatures were kept constant to within 0·01° C. With this arrangement it was possible to follow the progress of the diffusion and to study the approach to the steady state. Because of the large dimensions of the cell as compared with Tanner's the time required for a steady state to be reached was rather long—usually 3–6 days; and it seems likely from the results obtained that convection currents were not altogether eliminated, for his values of σ are always smaller than those of Tanner. A comparison of the two sets of results for HCl solutions is made in fig. 39.

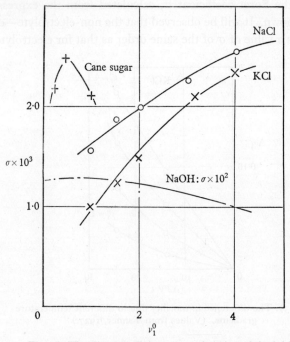

Fig. 38. The Soret coefficient σ as a function of the initial concentration ν_1^0. (Tanner, 1927.)

Some measurements of the effect in liquid alloys have been made by Ballay (1926, 1928), who has found a measurable separation due to thermal diffusion in the alloys of tin with copper, lead, cadmium and zinc. The alloys, in the fused state, were drawn into a silica tube, 14 cm. long and 1 cm. in diameter. After removal of air, the tube was sealed and then supported vertically with each end enclosed in a nickel block about 5 cm. long which was electrically heated. The lower part of the tube was thus brought to a temperature of usually 360° C. and the upper to a temperature between 600 and 900° C., these temperatures being maintained for 10 days or longer. The alloy was then rapidly cooled to solidification and the composition at either extremity determined chemically. It was found that in all four alloys the tin diffused up the temperature gradient whatever the initial composition of the alloy. Thus, for an alloy containing roughly equal molar proportions of lead and tin,

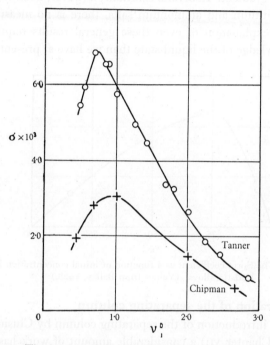

Fig. 39. The Soret coefficient as a function of the initial concentration, for HCl solutions. (Tanner, 1927 and Chipman, 1926.)

the proportion of tin in the hotter region at 700° C. exceeded by 8 % that in the cooler region at 360° C. Some results for lead-tin alloys are shown in fig. 40; for the other alloys the measurements are hardly numerous or consistent enough to establish more than the direction of the diffusion. Experiments such as these on metallic systems are of interest because they can cover a wider range of relative proportions and of temperature than is possible with aqueous solutions.

Only general conclusions can be drawn from the results of experiments made so far on thermal diffusion in the liquid state, and these apply only to aqueous solutions. It appears that in these solutions, thermal diffusion, if it occurs at all, is in such a direction that the solute concentrates in the colder region; the separation thus brought about is usually greater the greater the initial concentration of the solution; and, as expected, it increases with the temperature gradient. In several solutions, however, notably those containing lithium and ammonium salts, there is no measurable effect. The explanation of even these general results requires a greater knowledge of the liquid state than we have at present.

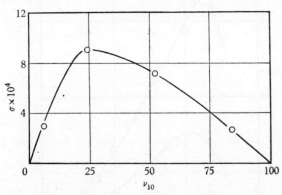

Fig. 40. The Soret coefficient as a function of initial concentration for lead-tin alloys. (Values from Ballay, 1928.)

8.4. Application of the separating column

Since the introduction of the separating column by Clusius and Dickel (cf. Chapter VII) a considerable amount of work has been done on its application to liquid mixtures. The first experiments reported were those of Korsching and Wirtz (1939), who used columns of both the coaxial tube and the hot-wire types with mixtures of some organic liquids. Clusius and Dickel (1939) themselves shortly after described the use of the column to effect large concentration changes in aqueous sodium chloride and other solutions.

The theory of the column as applied to the separation of liquid mixtures can be developed in a manner similar to that for the gaseous case. An account is given by de Groot (1945); more recently, Prigogine and others (1947, 1948) have discussed the theory of thermo-diffusion phenomena in general, including that of the separating column. The theory leads to an expression for the transport of a component up the column of the same form as that which applies to gas mixtures (7.5). When the optimum separation of the hot and cold surfaces is calculated from this expression, as was done in the gaseous case, it is found to be small—usually less than 1 mm.—and in consequence the influence of the height of the column on the separation achieved is much smaller than in the case of a gas mixture. Recent apparatus has therefore often taken the form of parallel plates separated by distances of between 0·1 and 1 mm., and of height only 10–20 cm. (Prigogine, de Brouckère and Amand, 1950). With such small separations, the transverse heat flux is large, and special attention must be paid to the transport of heat to and from the walls if the largest possible temperature gradient is to be maintained.

Of work done with the column, reference may be made first to that of Hirota (1941 a, b, 1942), who has examined the behaviour of binary solutions, chiefly electrolytes. The separation factors attained were in the sequence to be expected from the relative magnitudes of the Soret coefficients as measured directly. Docherty and Ritchie (1948) have studied the separation of aqueous solutions of several sugars—these solutions were chosen because their behaviour should be simpler than that of electrolytes, in which the ionic charges may affect the diffusion processes. More recently, Prigogine, de Brouckère and Amand (1950), in the hope of obtaining a further simplification, have experimented with mixtures in which both components were organic liquids with molecules of similar dimensions, for example, benzene and chlorobenzene. They have followed de Groot in determining the separation factor as a function of time and deducing therefrom experimental values of the quantities H and K which occur in the transport equation (cf. 7.6); both coefficients D and D' were then determined. The procedure is similar to that of McInteer, Aldrich and Nier in connexion with the helium isotopes (cf. p. 103), and no less liable to uncertainty because of the assumptions and approximations made in the theory.

FÜRTH'S ELEMENTARY THEORY OF THERMAL DIFFUSION

Derivation of the equation of diffusion. We have obtained for the diffusion velocity

$$\bar{c}_1 - \bar{c}_2 = \frac{\Gamma_1}{n_1} - \frac{\Gamma_2}{n_2} = \frac{\Gamma_1'}{n_1} - \frac{\Gamma_2'}{n_2}$$

$$= -\frac{1}{2}\left[\frac{1}{n_1}\frac{\partial n_1}{\partial z}\bar{z}_1\bar{C}_1 - \frac{1}{n_2}\frac{\partial n_2}{\partial z}\bar{z}_2\bar{C}_2 + \frac{\partial \bar{C}_1}{\partial z}\bar{z}_1' - \frac{\partial \bar{C}_2}{\partial z}\bar{z}_2'\right].$$

To reduce this to the form of (2.3) we proceed as follows. Since the partial pressure of molecules 1 is

$$n_{10}p = n_1 kT,$$

where p is the total pressure of the gas mixture,

$$\frac{\partial n_1}{\partial z} = \frac{p}{k}\left[\frac{1}{T}\frac{\partial n_{10}}{\partial z} - \frac{n_{10}}{T^2}\frac{\partial T}{\partial z}\right].$$

Also, neglecting the distinction between the mean speed $\bar{C}$ and the root-mean-square speed, we have

$$\bar{C} = \left(\frac{3kT}{m}\right)^{\frac{1}{2}},$$

so that

$$\frac{\partial \bar{C}_1}{\partial z} = \left(\frac{3k}{m}\right)^{\frac{1}{2}}\frac{1}{2T^{\frac{1}{2}}}\frac{\partial T}{\partial z}$$

and

$$\frac{1}{n_1}\frac{\partial n_1}{\partial z}\bar{C}_1\bar{z}_1 = \frac{p}{k}\left(\frac{3kT}{m}\right)^{\frac{1}{2}}\frac{1}{n_1}\left[\frac{1}{T}\frac{\partial n_{10}}{\partial z} - \frac{n_{10}}{T^2}\frac{\partial T}{\partial z}\right]\bar{z}_1$$

$$= \left(\frac{3k}{m}\right)^{\frac{1}{2}}\left[\frac{T^{\frac{1}{2}}}{n_{10}}\frac{\partial n_{10}}{\partial z} - \frac{1}{T^{\frac{1}{2}}}\frac{\partial T}{\partial z}\right]\bar{z}_1,$$

with a similar expression for molecules 2. Hence

$$\bar{c}_1 - \bar{c}_2 = -\tfrac{1}{2}(3kT)^{\frac{1}{2}}\left[\frac{\bar{z}_1}{n_{10}\sqrt{m_1}}\frac{\partial n_{10}}{\partial z} - \frac{\bar{z}_2}{n_{20}\sqrt{m_2}}\frac{\partial n_{20}}{\partial z}\right.$$
$$\left. - \left(\frac{\bar{z}_1}{\sqrt{m_1}} - \frac{\bar{z}_2}{\sqrt{m_2}}\right)\frac{1}{T}\frac{\partial T}{\partial z} + \left(\frac{\bar{z}_1'}{2\sqrt{m_1}} - \frac{\bar{z}_2'}{2\sqrt{m_2}}\right)\frac{1}{T}\frac{\partial T}{\partial z}\right]$$

$$= -\frac{(3kT)^{\frac{1}{2}}}{2}\left[\left(\frac{\bar{z}_1}{n_{10}\sqrt{m_1}} + \frac{\bar{z}_2}{n_{20}\sqrt{m_2}}\right)\frac{\partial n_{10}}{\partial z} - \left(\frac{\bar{z}_1 - \dfrac{\bar{z}_1'}{2}}{\sqrt{m_1}} - \frac{\bar{z}_2 - \dfrac{\bar{z}_2'}{2}}{\sqrt{m_2}}\right)\frac{1}{T}\frac{\partial T}{\partial z}\right]$$

$$= -\frac{1}{n_{10}n_{20}}\left[D_{12}\frac{\partial n_{10}}{\partial z} + D_T\frac{1}{T}\frac{\partial T}{\partial z}\right],$$

where $\qquad D_{12} = \dfrac{1}{2}\left(\dfrac{3kT}{m_1 m_2}\right)^{\frac{1}{2}}(\bar{z}_1 n_{20}\sqrt{m_2} + \bar{z}_2 n_{10}\sqrt{m_1})$

and $\quad D_T = -\dfrac{1}{2}\left(\dfrac{3kT}{m_1 m_2}\right)^{\frac{1}{2}}\left[\left(\bar{z}_1 - \dfrac{\bar{z}_1'}{2}\right)\sqrt{m_2} - \left(\bar{z}_2 - \dfrac{\bar{z}_2'}{2}\right)\sqrt{m_1}\right]n_{12}n_{20}.$

This expression for the diffusion velocity is formally identical with that derived rigorously by Chapman and Enskog.

The thermal diffusion ratio, k_T. Fürth shows that the correspondence with the rigorous theory may be further developed. Integration over all directions from which molecules approach the plane shows that $\bar{z} = \tfrac{2}{3}l$, where l is the mean free path for transference of number; similarly, $\bar{z}' = \tfrac{2}{3}l'$, where l' is the mean free path for transference of mean speed. Then

$$D_{12} = \left(\frac{kT}{3m_1 m_2}\right)^{\frac{1}{2}}(l_1\sqrt{m_2}\,n_{20} + l_2\sqrt{m_1}\,n_{10}),$$

and $\qquad k_T = \dfrac{\left(l_2 - \dfrac{l_2'}{2}\right)\sqrt{m_1} - \left(l_1 - \dfrac{l_1'}{2}\right)\sqrt{m_2}}{l_2\sqrt{m_1}\,n_{10} + l_1\sqrt{m_2}\,n_{20}}\,n_{10}n_{20}.$

Fürth now assumes that l_1 differs from l_1' and l_2 from l_2' only by a numerical factor a, so that

$$l_1' = al_1, \quad l_2' = al_2,$$

hence $\qquad k_T = \left(1 - \dfrac{a}{2}\right)\dfrac{\dfrac{\sqrt{m_1}}{l_1} - \dfrac{\sqrt{m_2}}{l_2}}{\dfrac{n_{10}\sqrt{m_1}}{l_1} + \dfrac{n_{20}\sqrt{m_2}}{l_2}}\,n_{10}n_{20}.$

Now if l_1 and l_2 are identified with the mean free path of Maxwell's elementary theory

$$\frac{1}{l_1} = \pi \left[\sqrt{2}\, n_1 \sigma_1^2 + n_2 \left(1 + \frac{m_1}{m_2} \right)^{\frac{1}{2}} \sigma_{12}^2 \right],$$

$$\frac{1}{l_2} = \pi \left[\sqrt{2}\, n_2 \sigma_2^2 + n_1 \left(1 + \frac{m_2}{m_1} \right)^{\frac{1}{2}} \sigma_{12}^2 \right],$$

where σ_1, σ_2 are the molecular diameters and $\sigma_{12} = \frac{1}{2}(\sigma_1 + \sigma_2)$. Substituting in the foregoing expression for k_T gives

$$k_T = \left(1 - \frac{a}{2} \right) \frac{a_1 n_{10} - a_2 n_{20}}{b_1 n_{10}^2 + b_2 n_{20}^2 + b_{12} n_{10} n_{20}}\, n_{10} n_{20},$$

with

$$a_1 = (2m_1)^{\frac{1}{2}} \sigma_1^2 - \left[\frac{m_2}{m_1}(m_1 + m_2) \right]^{\frac{1}{2}} \sigma_{12}^2,$$

$$a_2 = (2m_2)^{\frac{1}{2}} \sigma_2^2 - \left[\frac{m_1}{m_2}(m_1 + m_2) \right]^{\frac{1}{2}} \sigma_{12}^2,$$

$$b_1 = (2m_1)^{\frac{1}{2}} \sigma_1^2,$$

$$b_2 = (2m_2)^{\frac{1}{2}} \sigma_2^2,$$

$$b_{12} = \left[\frac{(m_1 + m_2)^3}{m_1 m_2} \right]^{\frac{1}{2}} \sigma_{12}^2.$$

This expression for k_T has the same form as in the rigorous theory (cf. Chapter II).

CALCULATION OF THE
THERMAL DIFFUSION FACTOR FOR
SPECIFIC MOLECULAR MODELS

Rigid elastic spheres. The values of the quantities A, B, C, E_1, E_2 in the expressions for S and Q (2.11) are

$$A = \tfrac{2}{5}, \ B = \tfrac{3}{5}, \ C = \tfrac{6}{5},$$

$$E_1 = \frac{16}{5(1-M)^{\frac{1}{2}}} \Sigma_1^2, \quad E_2 = \frac{16}{5(1+M)^{\frac{1}{2}}} \Sigma_2^2,$$

where $\Sigma_1 = \dfrac{\sigma_1}{\sigma_1 + \sigma_2}$, $\Sigma_2 = \dfrac{\sigma_2}{\sigma_1 + \sigma_2}$, σ_1 and σ_2 being the molecular diameters. Values of $[\alpha]_1$ for different values of M and Σ, $(\Sigma = \Sigma_1 - \Sigma_2)$, are shown graphically in fig. 7 (cf. also Appendix 7).

Inverse-power repulsion. For a mixture of isotopic molecules which repel each other with a force $F = \kappa r^{-\nu}$ (where r is the distance between the centres, κ is the force constant, and ν the force index) the values of A, B, C, E_1, E_2 are shown in Table IA. The values for $\nu = \infty$ correspond with those preceding for elastic spheres of equal diameters. Values of $[\alpha]_1$ for different values of M, ν, and relative proportions of the components, are shown graphically in fig. 8.

TABLE IA. *For inverse power repulsion, $F = \kappa r^{-\nu}$. Values of the quantities A, B, C etc. for various values of force index ν.*

ν	3	5	7	9	11	15	∞
A	0·531	0·517	0·493	0·477	0·465	0·450	0·400
B	0·800	0·750	0·711	0·687	0·672	0·653	0·600
C	0·800	1·00	1·967	1·100	1·120	1·143	1·200
$(1-M)^{\frac{1}{2}}E_1$ $=(1+M)^{\frac{1}{2}}E_2$	1·062	1·034	0·986	0·954	0·930	0·900	0·800

The Lennard-Jones model. The quantities A, B, C are here functions of the temperature. For the (13, 7) case, Hirschfelder, Bird and Spotz (1948) have given tables of the collision integrals and of the quantities A, B, C derived from them. A selection of these, which covers the range of temperature relevant to the experimental work is given in Table IIA. For the (9, 5) case the paper of Clark Jones (1941) may be consulted.

Values of $[\alpha]_1$ for molecules which have the same collision diameters σ are shown in fig. 10, and in Table IIIA.

TABLE IIA. *Values of A, B, C for the* (13, 7) *model*

kT/ϵ	A	B	C
0·3	0·4185	0·7739	1·017
0·5	0·4370	0·7698	0·9901
0·65	0·4409	0·752	0·9868
0·80	0·4418	0·734	0·9918
1·0	0·4410	0·715	1·004
1·25	0·4396	0·696	1·021
1·60	0·4382	0·683	1·042
2·0	0·4374	0·671	1·061
2·5	0·4374	0·664	1·079
4·0	0·4391	0·657	1·109
6·0	0·413	0·656	1·125
10	0·441	0·657	1·134
20	0·4477	0·6569	1·137
30	0·4496	0·6569	1·138
40	0·4508	0·6574	1·138

TABLE IIIA. *Values of R_T for molecules of the Lennard-Jones* (13, 7) *type, having the same collision diameters. (The values are for mixtures of equal proportions, $n_{10} = n_{20} = 0·5$)*

Values of $[\alpha]_1$ can be derived from R_T by multiplying by $0·89M$ when $M \to 0$, $0·38_1$ when $M = 0·5$, $0·53_6$ when $M = 1·0$.

	kT/ϵ	0·3	0·4	0·5	0·65	0·8	1·0	1·25	1·60
R_T	$M \to 0$	0·086	−0·002	−0·048	−0·063	−0·032	0·019	0·099	0·197
	$M = 0·5$	—	—	—	−0·067	−0·041	0·020	0·103	0·206
	$M = 1·0$	0·102	−0·003	−0·058	−0·076	−0·046	0·022	0·113	0·223

	kT/ϵ	2·00	2·5	3·2	4·0	5·0	6	8	10
R_T	$M \to 0$	0·286	0·370	0·447	0·506	0·547	0·578	0·604	0·616
	$M = 0·5$	0·297	0·384	0·463	0·525	0·567	0·600	0·627	0·640
	$M = 1·0$	0·320	0·412	0·496	0·563	0·607	0·643	0·674	0·689

	kT/ϵ	20	30	40	50	80	100	200	300
R_T	$M \to 0$	0·625	0·627	0·625	0·623	0·621	0·619	0·615	0·612
	$M = 0·5$	0·650	0·653	0·652	0·650	—	—	—	—
	$M = 1·0$	0·702	0·707	0·706	0·705	0·704	0·704	0·702	0·701

THE APPROACH TO THE STEADY STATE

The manner in which the steady state is approached when the diffusion vessel is of the usual two-bulb form has been discussed by Clark Jones and Furry (1946). Their treatment is essentially what follows.

The equation of diffusion

$$\bar{\mathbf{c}}_1 - \bar{\mathbf{c}}_2 = -\frac{D_{12}}{n_{10}n_{20}}\left[\frac{\partial n_{10}}{\partial \mathbf{r}} + k_T \frac{1}{T}\frac{\partial T}{\partial \mathbf{r}}\right]$$

may be written in terms of the mean velocity $\bar{\mathbf{c}} = n_{10}\bar{\mathbf{c}}_1 + n_{20}\bar{\mathbf{c}}_2$ as

$$n_{10}(\bar{\mathbf{c}}_1 - \bar{\mathbf{c}}) = -D_{12}\left[\frac{\partial n_{10}}{\partial \mathbf{r}} + k_T \frac{1}{T}\frac{\partial T}{\partial \mathbf{r}}\right].$$

In the experimental method the gas as a whole is at rest, that is, $\bar{\mathbf{c}} = 0$; then, if we take the temperature gradient as being in the z direction,

$$n_{10}\bar{c}_1 = -D_{12}\left[\frac{\partial n_{10}}{\partial z} + k_T \frac{1}{T}\frac{\partial T}{\partial z}\right].$$

If the temperature gradient is uniform

$$\frac{\partial T}{\partial z} = \frac{\Delta T}{L},$$

where $\Delta T = T' - T$, the difference in temperature of the two bulbs, and L is the length of the connecting tube. Replacing k_T by its average value $\bar{k}_T$ over the length of the tube, we obtain

$$n_{10}\bar{c}_1 = -\frac{D_{12}}{L}\frac{\Delta T}{T}\left[T\frac{\partial n_{10}}{\partial T} + \bar{k}_T\right],$$

or

$$n_1\bar{c}_1 = -\frac{nD_{12}}{T}\frac{\Delta T}{L}\left[T\frac{\partial n_{10}}{\partial T} + \bar{k}_T\right].$$

$n_1\bar{c}_1$ is the flux density of molecules of species 1 along the connecting tube. The equation of continuity for these molecules is

$$\frac{\partial}{\partial z}(n_1\bar{c}_1) = -\frac{\partial n_1}{\partial t}.$$

Here the assumption is made that conditions are quasi-stationary, that is, that the rate of change of density $\partial n_1/\partial t$ is small; this is so if the volume of the bulbs is large compared with that of the connecting tube. When this condition is satisfied $\partial(n_1\bar{c}_1)/\partial z \to 0$ and the flux density is the same throughout the tube.

Now n, the number density of both species, is inversely proportional to the temperature T, and the coefficient D_{12} varies approximately as T^2; nD_{12}/T is therefore independent of T. The equation can therefore be integrated to give

$$n_1\bar{c}_1 = -\frac{nD_{12}}{T}\frac{\Delta T}{L}\left[\frac{n'_{10}-n_{10}}{\ln(T'/T)}+\bar{k}_T\right]$$

$$= \frac{nD_{12}}{T}\frac{\Delta T}{L}\left[\frac{\Delta n_{10}}{\ln(T'/T)}-\bar{k}_T\right],$$

writing $n_{10}-n'_{10}=\Delta n_{10}$.

The flux of molecules 1 along the tube, if this has cross-sectional area σ, is $n_1\bar{c}_1\sigma$, and the rate of change of composition in the bulb at temperature T, containing N molecules in all, is

$$\left(\frac{\partial n_{10}}{\partial t}\right)_T = -\frac{n_1\bar{c}_1\sigma}{N},$$

and in the bulb at temperature T', containing N' molecules, is

$$\left(\frac{\partial n_{10}}{\partial t}\right)_{T'} = +\frac{n_1\bar{c}_1\sigma}{N'}.$$

Hence $$\frac{\partial(\Delta n_{10})}{\partial t} = -n_1\bar{c}_1\sigma\left(\frac{1}{N}+\frac{1}{N'}\right).$$

Substituting for $n_1\bar{c}_1$ its value above

$$\frac{\partial(\Delta n_{10})}{\partial t} = -\frac{nD_{12}}{T}\frac{\Delta T\sigma}{L}\left[\frac{\Delta n_{10}}{\ln(T'/T)}-\bar{k}_T\right]\left[\frac{1}{N}+\frac{1}{N'}\right],$$

or $$\frac{\partial(\Delta n_{10})}{\partial t} = a - b\,\Delta n_{10},$$

where a, b are constants. The solution is

$$\Delta n_{10} = S(1-e^{-bt}),$$

since $\Delta n_{10} = 0$ when $t = 0$, and $\Delta n_{10} = S$, the separation, when $t = \infty$. The approach to the steady state is therefore exponential. The relaxation time, that is the time required for Δn_{10} to attain $(1 - 1/e)$ of its final value, is

$$\tau = 1/b = \frac{NN'}{N+N'} \frac{L}{nD_{12}\sigma} \frac{T}{\Delta T} \ln(T'/T).$$

τ is thus proportional to the length of the connecting tube, and inversely proportional to its cross-sectional area. τ depends on the pressure only through the coefficient D_{12}; as this is inversely proportional to the pressure, τ varies directly with the pressure.

That the approach to the steady state is approximately exponential is confirmed by some measurements (about to be published) made by Nettley.

APPENDIX 4

IDENTIFICATION OF THE MEAN VALUE OF THE THERMAL DIFFUSION FACTOR WITH THE ACTUAL VALUE FOR A SPECIFIC TEMPERATURE

When the separation is small, as with isotopic mixtures, it is necessary to have the two bulbs of the diffusion vessel at widely different temperatures T, T'. The separation is then measurable but from it only a mean value of the thermal diffusion factor in the range $T \to T'$ can be found. Harrison Brown (1940) has shown how this mean value, $\bar{\alpha}$, can be identified with the actual value of α at a specific temperature T_r within the range $T \to T'$.

It is assumed that α varies with temperature according to the relation

$$\alpha = \alpha_0(1 - A/T),$$

where A is a constant and α_0 is the limiting value of α at high temperatures. This relation does in fact represent fairly well the variation of α with temperature found experimentally in many cases, and also in the theoretical case of the Lennard-Jones $(13, 7)$ model. The separation over the range $T \to T'$ is then

$$S = \int_T^{T'} \alpha n_{10} n_{20} d(\ln T).$$

The mean value of α is found experimentally as the ratio

$$\bar{\alpha} = S/\{n_{10} n_{20} \ln (T'/T)\},$$

hence

$$\bar{\alpha} = \frac{\int_T^{T'} \alpha \, d(\ln T)}{\ln (T'/T)} = \frac{\int_T^{T'} \alpha_0(1 - A/T) \, d(\ln T)}{\ln (T'/T)}$$

$$= \alpha_0 \left[1 - \frac{A}{\dfrac{TT'}{T' - T} \ln \dfrac{T'}{T}} \right] = \alpha_0 \left[1 - \frac{A}{T_r} \right],$$

so that the mean value corresponds with the actual value of α at the temperature

$$T_r = \frac{TT'}{T' - T} \ln \frac{T'}{T}.$$

APPENDIX 5

TABLE IV A. *Comparison of the values of R_T calculated for the (13, 7) model and the experimental values*

Experimental values for neon and argon isotopes Stier (1942); for oxygen isotopes Whalley and Winter (1949); others Grew (1947, 1949).

Mixture	$[\alpha(\infty)]_1$	ϵ_{12}/k, $\sigma_{12}A.$		Temperature ° K.						
				150	200	250	300	400	500	600
He-Ne,	0·498	14·7	$10R_T$ (13, 7)	6·60	6·65	6·68	6·70	6·74	6·75	6·73
53·8 % He		2·75	$10R_T$ (exp.)	6·06	6·3	6·4	6·4	6·4	6·4	6·4
He-A,	0·60	27·3	$10R_T$ (13, 7)	6·00	6·40	6·55	6·63	6·73	6·75	6·75
51·2 % He		3·06	$10R_T$ (exp.)	5·75	6·2	6·4	6·4	6·5	6·55	6·6
He-Kr,	0·67	33·8	$10R_T$ (13, 7)	5·65	6·10	6·35	6·50	6·65	6·70	6·70
55·0 % He		3·16	$10R_T$ (exp.)	6·1	6·5	6·7	6·7	6·7	6·7	6·7
He-X,	0·65	37·2	$10R_T$ (13, 7)	—	—	6·60	6·75	6·95	7·00	7·00
53·6 % He		3·38	$10R_T$ (exp.)	—	—	6·6	6·6	6·6	6·6	6·6
Ne-A,	0·34	66·5	$10R_T$ (13, 7)	3·35	4·35	4·95	5·30	5·75	5·95	6·05
51·2 % Ne		3·11	$10R_T$ (exp.)	3·6	4·4	5·0	5·3	5·6	5·7	5·7
Ne-Kr,	0·53	82·4	$10R_T$ (13, 7)	2·58	3·75	4·50	5·02	5·62	5·95	6·12
53·0 % Ne		3·20	$10R_T$ (exp.)	3·4	4·3	5·0	5·5	6·0	6·2	6·4
Ne-X,	0·61	90·6	$10R_T$ (13, 7)	—	3·45	4·28	4·80	5·50	5·92	6·12
54·2 % Ne		3·42	$10R_T$ (exp.)	—	4·4	4·7	4·8	5·5	6·1	6·6
A-Kr,	0·32	153·5	$10R_T$ (13, 7)	0·15	1·15	2·08	2·85	3·90	4·50	4·98
53·5 % A		3·51	$10R_T$ (exp.)	0·8	1·4	2·0	3·4	3·8	5·0	6·2
A-X,	0·47	168·9	$10R_T$ (13, 7)	—	0·82	1·72	2·50	3·56	4·22	4·73
56·4 % A		3·73	$10R_T$ (exp.)	—	1·4	1·6	2·2	3·2	4·0	4·6
H_2-N_2,	0·53	54·2	$10R_T$ (13, 7)	4·48	5·30	5·80	6·12	6·50	6·68	6·75
39·8 % H_2		3·32	$10R_T$ (exp.)	3·8	4·8	5·4	5·6	5·8	5·9	6·0
H_2-CO_2,	0·60	79·5	$10R_T$ (13, 7)	—	—	5·00	5·54	6·20	6·55	—
49·0 % H_2		3·48	$10R_T$ (exp.)	—	—	3·6	4·2	5·2	5·5	—
^{20}Ne-^{22}Ne,	—	35·7	$10R_T$ (13, 7)	5·2	5·65	5·90	6·02	6·14	6·20	6·22
90·1 % ^{20}Ne		2·80	$10R_T$ (exp.)	4·4	5·0	5·6	6·0	6·8	7·4	7·8
^{36}A-^{40}A,	—	124·0	$10R_T$ (13, 7)	0·85	2·00	2·88	3·57	4·52	5·10	5·43
0·31 % ^{36}A		3·42	$10R_T$ (exp.)	1·2	2·0	2·6	3·1	3·9	4·4	4·9

For isotopic hydrogen, nitrogen, oxygen, methane: see Table III, p. 53, and Table IV, p. 54.

APPENDIX 6

TABLE VA. *List of mixtures examined experimentally.*
For reference key see p. 131

The values of α and R_T are for mixtures of equal proportions. When a temperature range is given, α and R_T are mean values in this range; when a single temperature is given α and R_T are for this temperature.

Mixture	References	m_1/m_2	Temp. range $T \to T'$ °K.	α	R_T and Reference
H_2-D_2	(6a), (8), (11d) (14)	2·00	288–373 273–360	0·173 $\begin{cases} 0·149 \\ 20\%\,D_2 \end{cases}$	0·61 (8) 0·50 (14)
H_2-HD	(17a)	—	—	—	—
H_2-He	(5), (6c), (8)	2·00	273–760 90–600	0·15$_2$ —	0·63 (5) 0·59 (6c)
	(11a), (11d), (14)	—	292–90 292–20	0·137 0·140	0·58 (11a) 0·59 (11a)
H_2-CH_4	(4)	7·96	300–523 300–190	0·288 0·222	— (4) — (4)
H_2-H_2O	(17b)	8·95	—	—	—
H_2-Ne	(10c), (11a), (11b), (11c)	10·0	288–128 290–90 290–20	0·36 0·280 0·174	0·73 (10c) 0·57 (11c) 0·34 (11c)
H_2-CO	(10a), (10b), (11a)	13·9	288–373 293–90	0·33$_0$ 0·21$_6$	0·58 (10a) 0·38 (11a)
H_2-N_2	(3), (6d), (9), (10a), (10b), (11a), (11b), (19a), (19c)	13·9	288–456 288–373 292–90 293	0·31$_2$ 0·34$_0$ 0·24 0·28	0·55 (9) 0·60 (10a) 0·42 (11a) 0·49 (19a)
H_2-C_2H_4	(4), (10b)	13·9	300–523 200–190 288–373	0·27$_7$ 0·241 0·32	— (4) — (4) — (10a)
H_2-O_2	(10b), (11a)	15·9	294–90	0·192	— (11a)
H_2-A	(9), (10b), (11b), (19a)	19·8	288–456 286–108 292–90 293	0·28 0·22 0·19$_1$ 0·28	0·49 (9) 0·39 (10b) 0·33 (11b) 0·49 (19a)
H_2-C_3H_6	(4)	20·9	300–523 232–376	0·305 0·284	— (4) — (4)
H_2-C_3H_8	(4)	21·9	300–523 231–375	0·315 0·291	— (4) — (4)
H_2-CO_2	(2), (3), (5), (9), (10a), (10b), (12), (19a)	21·8	288–456 288–373 300–400	0·284 0·29$_8$ 0·27$_2$	0·47 (9) 0·49 (10a) 0·45 (16)
H_2-N_2O	(2), (10a), (10b)	21·8	—	—	—
H_2-Rn	(7a)	110	273–373	0·31	0·15 (7a)
D_2-He	(14)	1·01	—	—	—
D_2-Ne	(11c)	5·00	—	—	—

TABLE V A (*continued*)

Mixture	References	m_1/m_2	Temp. range $T \to T'$ °K	α	R_T and Reference
D_2-N_2	(6d), (11b)	6·95	287–373	0·313	0·58 (6d)
D_2-A	(11b)	9·9	—	—	—
^{3}He-^{4}He	(15d)	1·33	273–613	0·05$_9$	0·49 (15d)
He-Ne	(1), (6b), (10c)	5·06	288–373	0·38$_8$	0·79 (1)
			300–400	0·36$_4$	0·75 (16)
	(11a), (11b), (11c), (16)	—	200–600	0·31$_6$	0·65 (6b)
			293–90	0·33$_0$	0·68 (11c)
			293–20	0·24$_2$	0·49 (11c)
He-N_2	(6d), (10c)	7·00	287–373	0·36	0·62 (6d)
He-A	(1), (6b), (9), (10c), (11b), (16)	9·98	288–373	0·37$_2$	0·62 (1)
			300–400	0·42	0·71 (16)
			185	0·36	0·61 (6b)
			293	0·38	0·64 (6b)
			369	0·39	0·65 (6b)
			273–90	0·31	0·52 (11b)
He-CO_2	(5)	11·0	—	—	—
He-Kr	(1), (6b)	20·9	288–373	0·40$_0$	0·64 (1)
			185	0·43	0·64 (6b)
			293	0·44$_8$	0·67 (6b)
			369	0·44$_8$	0·67 (6b)
			465	0·44$_8$	0·67 (6b)
He-Xe	(1), (6b)	32·8	288–373	0·40$_3$	0·62 (1)
			233	0·43	0·66 (6b)
			293	0·43$_4$	0·66 (6b)
			369	0·43$_4$	0·66 (6b)
			465	0·43$_4$	0·66 (6b)
He-Rn	(7a)	55·5	273–373	0·64	0·23 (7a)
$^{12}CH_4$-$^{13}CH_4$	(15), (21b)	1·06	—	—	—
$^{14}NH_3$-$^{15}NH_3$	(20)	1·06	366	+0·010	+0·41 (20)
			268	−0·004	−0·15
			239	−0·010	−0·39
^{20}Ne-^{22}Ne	(13), (15), (18)	1·10	691–819	0·0346	0·82 (18)
			460–638	0·0318	0·75 (18)
			302–645	0·0302	0·71 (18)
			195–490	0·0254	0·60 (18)
			195–296	0·0233	0·55 (18)
			90–296	0·0187	0·44 (18)
			90–195	0·0162	0·39 (18)
Ne-A	(1), (6b), (10c)	1·98	288–373	0·18$_1$	0·55 (1)
			185	0·148	0·44 (6b)
			293	0·17$_4$	0·52 (6b)
			369	0·19	0·57 (6b)
			465	0·191	0·57 (6b)
Ne-Kr	(1), (6b)	4·15	288–373	0·26$_7$	0·52 (1)
			185	0·21	0·40 (6b)
			293	0·29	0·55 (6b)
			369	0·31	0·59 (6b)
			465	0·32	0·61 (6b)

TABLE VA (continued)

Mixture	References	m_1/m_2	Temp. range $T \to T'$ °K.	α	R_T and Reference
Ne-Xe	(1), (6b)	6·51	288–373	0·25₃	0·43 (1)
			185	0·26	0·43 (6b)
			293	0·30	0·49 (6b)
			369	0·33	0·54 (6b)
			465	0·37	0·60 (6b)
Ne-Rn	(7b)	11·0	273–373	0·23	0·12 (7b)
CO-CO₂	(10a)	1·57	—	—	—
CO-N₂O	(10a)	1·57	—	—	—
C₂H₄-N₂	(19c)	1·00	—	—	—
C₂H₄-O₂	(19c)	1·14	—	—	—
C₂H₄-A	(19c)	1·42	—	—	—
¹⁴N₂-¹⁴, ¹⁵N₂	(13), (21b)	—	195–623	0·0051	0·33 (13)
N₂-O₂	(19b)	1·14	293	0·018	— (19b)
			89	<0·001	— (19b)
N₂-A	(10b), (19a), (19b), (19c)	1·42	293	0·071	— (19b)
			89	0·035	— (19b)
N₂-CO₂	(2), (9), (10a), (19c)	1·57	288–400	0·050	0·22 (2)
			288–373	0·06₁	0·26 (10a)
			283	0·036	0·15 (19c)
			372	0·051	0·22 (19c)
N₂-N₂O	(2), (10a)	1·57	288–400	0·048	0·20 (2)
¹⁶, ¹⁶O₂-¹⁶, ¹⁸O₂	(21), (21a)	1·06	264	0·0099	0·37 (21)
			389	0·0128	0·48 (21)
			443	0·0145	0·54 (21)
O₂-A	(19a), (19b), (19c)	—	283	0·05₀	— (19a,c)
O₂-CO₂	(10a), (19c)	1·38	—	—	—
O₂-N₂O	(10a)	1·38	—	—	—
³⁶A-⁴⁰A	(13), (18)	1·11	638–835	0·0250	0·53 (18)
			455–635	0·0218	0·47 (18)
			273–623	0·0182	0·39 (18)
			195–495	0·0146	0·31 (18)
			195–296	0·0116	0·25 (18)
			90–296	0·0071	0·15 (18)
			90–195	0·0031	0·07 (18)
A-CO₂	(19c)	1·10	283	0·019	— (19c)
A-Kr	(1), (6b)	2·10	288–373	0·055	0·18 (1)
			185	0·038	0·12 (6b)
			294	0·075	0·24 (6b)
			370	0·10₄	0·33 (6b)
			465	0·14₉	0·47 (6b)
A-Xe	(1), (6b)	3·29	288–373	0·077	0·17 (1)
			185	0·063	0·13 (6b)
			294	0·087	0·18 (6b)
			369	0·139	0·29 (6b)
			465	0·176	0·37 (6b)
A-Rn	(7b)	5·56	273–373	0·024	0·023 (7b)
Kr-Xe	(1)	1·57	288–373	0·016	0·08 (1)

Key to References in TABLE VA

(1) Atkins, Bastick and Ibbs (1939).

(2) Bastick, Heath and Ibbs (1939).

(3) Blüh, O. and G. (1934).

(4) Drickamer, Downey and Pierce (1949).

(5) Elliott and Masson (1925).

(6) (a) Grew (1941).
    (b) Grew (1947).
    (c) Grew (1949).
    (d) Grew and Atkins (1936).

(7) (a) Harrison (1937).
    (b) Harrison (1942).

(8) Heath, Ibbs and Wild (1941).

(9) Ibbs (1925).

(10) (a) Ibbs and Underwood (1927).
    (b) Ibbs, Grew and Hirst (1929).
    (c) Ibbs and Grew (1931).

(11) (a) van Itterbeek, van Paemel, van Lierde (1947).
    (b) van Itterbeek and de Troyer (1950).
    (c) de Troyer, van Itterbeek and van den Berg (1950).
    (d) de Troyer, van Itterbeek and Rietveld (1951).

(12) Lugg (1929).

(13) Mann (1948).

(14) Murphey (1947).

(15) (a) Nier (1939).
    (b) Nier (1940a).
    (c) Nier (1940b).
    (d) McInteer, Aldrich and Nier (1947).

(16) Puschner (1937).

(17) (a) Kitagawa (1941).
    (b) Shibata and Kitagawa (1938).

(18) Stier (1942).

(19) (a) Waldmann (1947a).
    (b) Waldmann (1947c).
    (c) Waldmann (1949).

(20) Watson and Woernley (1943).

(21) (a) Whalley, Winter and Briscoe (1949).
    (b) Davenport and Winter (1951).

APPENDIX 7

TABLE VI A. *Calculated values of the thermal diffusion factor*
for mixtures examined experimentally when the
molecules are treated as rigid spheres

m_1/m_2 = mass ratio; σ_1/σ_2 = diameter ratio; S, Q = quantities in the expression for α (2.11); $[\alpha(\infty)]_1$ = the thermal diffusion factor for mixtures of equal proportions.

Mixture	Mass ratio m_1/m_2	Diameter ratio σ_1/σ_2	$S_1, -S_2, Q_1, Q_2, Q_{12}$	$[\alpha(\infty)]_1$
H_2-D_2	2·00	1·00	0·438, 0·550, 1·724, 1·764, 3·668	0·276
-He	2·00	0·80	0·341, 0·511, 1·355, 2·186, 3·642	0·237
-Ne	10·0	0·95	0·443, 0·595, 1·131, 0·845, 2·213	0·495
-CO	13·9	1·38	0·550, 0·487, 1·430, 0·438, 1·784	0·568
-N_2	13·9	1·38	0·550, 0·487, 1·430, 0·438, 1·784	0·568
-O_2	15·9	1·33	0·510, 0·443, 1·320, 0·405, 1·630	0·568
-A	19·8	1·34	0·470, 0·378, 1·220, 0·338, 1·411	0·571
-CO_2	21·8	1·70	0·540, 0·348, 1·409, 0·232, 1·275	0·609
D_2-N_2	6·95	1·36	0·685, 0·715, 1·817, 0·733, 2·667	0·537
He-Ne	5·06	1·19	0·638, 0·783, 1·713, 1·046, 3·062	0·488
-N_2	7·00	1·73	0·805, 0·718, 2·137, 0·554, 2·584	0·577
-A	9·98	1·69	0·718, 0·603, 1·879, 0·444, 2·139	0·592
-Kr	20·9	1·92	0·602, 0·361, 1·570, 0·207, 1·296	0·627
-Xe	32·8	2·24	0·550, 0·248, 1·433, 0·113, 0·899	0·652
Ne-A	1·98	1·40	0·603, 0·593, 2·368, 1·214, 3·616	0·332
-Kr	4·15	1·57	0·805, 0·813, 2·260, 0·839, 3·194	0·514
-X	6·51	1·85	0·858, 0·740, 2·290, 0·532, 2·652	0·584
N_2-CO_2	1·57	1·23	0·408, 0·418, 2·154, 1·480, 3·38	0·236
A-Kr	2·10	1·14	0·515, 0·600, 1·931, 1·539, 3·653	0·313
-Xe	3·29	1·33	0·705, 0·792, 2·075, 1·124, 3·425	0·452
Kr-Xe	1·57	1·18	0·390, 0·405, 2·081, 1·537, 3·673	0·218

REFERENCES

Note. Reference to *The Mathematical Theory of Non-Uniform Gases* by Chapman and Cowling is indicated by (*M.T.*).

ATKINS, B. E., BASTICK, R. E. and IBBS, T. L. (1939). *Proc. Roy. Soc.* A, **172**, 142.

BALLAY, M. (1926). *C.R. Acad. Sci., Paris*, **183**, 603.
BALLAY, M. (1928). *Rev. Métall.* **25**, 427.
BARDEEN, J. (1940). *Phys. Rev.* **57**, 35.
BASTICK, R. E., HEATH, H. R. and IBBS, T. L. (1939). *Proc. Roy. Soc.* A, **173**, 543.
BECKER, E. W. (1950). *Z. Naturforsch.* **5**a, 457.
BLÜH, G. and O. (1934). *Z. Phys.* **90**, 12.
DE BOER, J. and VAN KRANENDONK, J. (1948). *Physica*, **14**, 442.
BOLLAND, J. L. and MELVILLE, H. W. (1937). *Trans. Faraday Soc.* **33**, 1316.
BORN, M. and GREEN, H. S. (1946). *Proc. Roy. Soc.* A, **188**, 10.
BORN, M. and GREEN, H. S. (1947). *Proc. Roy. Soc.* A, **190**, 455; A, **191**, 168.
BROWN, HARRISON (1940). *Phys. Rev.* **58**, 661.

CHAPMAN, S. (1912). *Philos. Trans.* A, **211**, 433.
CHAPMAN, S. (1916a). *Philos. Trans.* A, **216**, 279.
CHAPMAN, S. (1916b). *Proc. Roy. Soc.* A, **93**, 1.
CHAPMAN, S. (1917a). *Philos. Trans.* A, **217**, 115.
CHAPMAN, S. (1917b). *Phil. Mag.* [6] **34**, 146.
CHAPMAN, S. (1919). *Phil. Mag.* [6] **38**, 182.
CHAPMAN, S. (1928a). *Proc. Roy. Soc.* A, **119**, 34.
CHAPMAN, S. (1928b). *Phil. Mag.* [7] **5**, 630.
CHAPMAN, S. (1929). *Phil. Mag.* [7] **7**, 1.
CHAPMAN, S. (1940a). *Nature, Lond.*, **146**, 131.
CHAPMAN, S. (1940b). *Proc. Roy. Soc.* A, **177**, 38.
CHAPMAN, S. and COWLING, T. G. (1939). *Mathematical Theory of Non-Uniform Gases.* Cambridge University Press.
CHAPMAN, S. and DOOTSON, F. W. (1917). *Phil. Mag.* [6] **33**, 248.
CHAPMAN, S. and HAINSWORTH, W. (1924). *Phil. Mag.* [6] **48**, 593.
CHIPMAN, J. (1926). *J. Amer. Chem. Soc.* **48**, 2577.
CLARK JONES, R. (1940). *Phys. Rev.* **58**, 111.
CLARK JONES, R. (1941). *Phys. Rev.* **59**, 1019.
CLARK JONES, R. and FURRY, W. H. (1946). *Rev. Mod. Phys.* **18**, 151.
CLUSIUS, K. (1949). *Helv. Phys. Acta*, **22**, 473.
CLUSIUS, K. and BECKER, E. W. (1947). *Z. Naturforsch.* **2**a, 154.
CLUSIUS, K. and DICKEL, G. (1938). *Naturwissenschaften*, **26**, 546.
CLUSIUS, K. and DICKEL, G. (1939). *Naturwissenschaften*, **27**, 148.
CLUSIUS, K. and DICKEL, G. (1940). *Naturwissenschaften*, **28**, 711.

CURTISS, C. F. and HIRSCHFELDER, J. O. (1949). *J. Chem. Phys.* **17**, 550.

DAVENPORT, A. N. and WINTER, E. R. S. (1951). *Trans. Faraday Soc.* **47**, 1160.

DAYNES, H. A. (1920). *Proc. Roy. Soc.* A, **97**, 273.

DOCHERTY, A. C. and RITCHIE, M. (1948). *Proc. Roy. Soc. Edinb.* A, **62**, 297.

DRICKAMER, H. G., DOWNEY, S. L. and PIERCE, N. C. (1949). *J. Chem. Phys.* **17**, 408.

DRICKAMER, H. G. and HOFTO, J. R. (1949). *J. Chem. Phys.* **17**, 1165.

DUFOUR, L. (1873). *Pogg. Ann.* **148**, 490.

ELLIOTT, G. A. and MASSON, I. (1925). *Proc. Roy. Soc.* A, **108**, 378.

ENSKOG, D. (1911). *Phys. Z.* **12**, 56, 533.

ENSKOG, D. (1912). *Ann. Phys., Lpz.*, **38**, 731.

ENSKOG, D. (1917). Dissertation (Uppsala).

ENSKOG, D. (1922). *Ark. Mat. Astr. Fys.* **16**, no. 16.

ENSKOG, D. (1928). *Ark. Mat. Astr. Fys.* **21** A, no. 13.

FRANKEL, S. P. (1940). *Phys. Rev.* **57**, 661.

FURRY, W. H. (1948). *Amer. J. Phys.* **16**, 63.

FURRY, W. H. and JONES, R. C. (1946). *Phys. Rev.* **69**, 459.

FURRY, W. H., JONES, R. C. and ONSAGER, L. (1939). *Phys. Rev.* **55**, 1083.

FÜRTH, R. (1942). *Proc. Roy. Soc.* A, **179**, 461.

GILLESPIE, L. J. (1939). *J. Chem. Phys.* **7**, 530.

GREW, K. E. (1941). *Proc. Roy. Soc.* A, **178**, 390.

GREW, K. E. (1942). *Nature, Lond.*, **150**, 320.

GREW, K. E. (1944). *Phil. Mag.* [7] **35**, 30.

GREW, K. E. (1945). *Nature, Lond.*, **156**, 267.

GREW, K. E. (1947). *Proc. Roy. Soc.* A, **189**, 402.

GREW, K. E. (1949). *Proc. Phys. Soc.* **62**, 655.

GREW, K. E. and ATKINS, B. E. (1936). *Proc. Phys. Soc.* **48**, 415.

VAN DER GRINTEN, W. (1939). *Naturwissenschaften*, **27**, 317.

DE GROOT, S. R. (1945). *L'Effet Soret.* Amsterdam.

GROTH, W. and HARTECK, P. (1939). *Naturwissenschaften*, **27**, 584.

GROTH, W. and HARTECK, P. (1940). *Naturwissenschaften*, **28**, 47.

HARRISON, G. E. (1937). *Proc. Roy. Soc.* A, **161**, 80.

HARRISON, G. E. (1942). *Proc. Roy. Soc.* A, **181**, 93.

HASSÉ, H. R. and COOK, W. R. (1929). *Proc. Roy. Soc.* A, **125**, 196.

HEATH, H. R., IBBS, T. L. and WILD, N. E. (1941). *Proc. Roy. Soc.* A, **178**, 380.

HELLUND, E. J. (1940). *Phys. Rev.* **57**, 319, 328.

HELLUND, E. J. and UEHLING, E. A. (1939). *Phys. Rev.* **56**, 818.

HIROTA, K. (1941*a*). *J. Chem. Soc. Japan*, **62**, 480.

HIROTA, K. (1941*b*). *Bull. Chem. Soc. Japan*, **16**, 475.

HIROTA, K. (1942). *J. Chem. Soc. Japan*, **63**, 105, 999.

HIRSCHFELDER, J. O., BIRD, R. B. and SPOTZ, E. L. (1948). *J. Chem. Phys.* **16**, 968.

HIRSCHFELDER, J. O., BIRD, R. B. and SPOTZ, E. L. (1949). *Chem. Rev.* **44**, 205.

HIRSCHFELDER, J. O. and ROSEVEARE (1939). *J. Phys. Chem.* **43**, 15.
VAN'T HOFF, J. H. (1887). *Z. Phys. Chem.* **1**, 481.

IBBS, T. L. (1921). *Proc. Roy. Soc.* A, **99**, 385.
IBBS, T. L. (1925). *Proc. Roy. Soc.* A, **107**, 470.
IBBS, T. L. and GREW, K. E. (1931). *Proc. Phys. Soc.* **43**, 142.
IBBS, T. L., GREW, K. E. and HIRST, A. A. (1929). *Proc. Phys. Soc.* **41**, 456.
IBBS, T. L. and UNDERWOOD, L. (1927). *Proc. Phys. Soc.* **39**, 227.
VAN ITTERBEEK, A. and VAN PAEMEL, O. (1938). *Physica*, **5**, 1004.
VAN ITTERBEEK, A. and VAN PAEMEL, O. (1940). *Physica*, **7**, 265.
VAN ITTERBEEK, A., VAN PAEMEL, O. and VAN LIERDE, J. (1947). *Physica*, **13**, 231.
VAN ITTERBEEK, A. and DE TROYER, A. (1950). *Physica*, **16**, 329.

JEANS, SIR JAMES (1940). *An Introduction to the Kinetic Theory of Gases.* Cambridge University Press.
JOHNSTON, H. L. and GRILLY, E. R. (1942). *J. Phys. Chem.* **46**, 948.
JOHNSTON, H. L. and McCLOSKEY, J. (1940). *J. Phys. Chem.* **44**, 1038.
JONES, R. C. *see* CLARK JONES

KITAGAWA, H. (1941). *J. Chem. Soc. Japan*, **61**, 1243.
KORSCHING, H. and WIRTZ, L. (1939). *Naturwissenschaften*, **27**, 110.

LAUDER, I. (1947). *Trans. Faraday Soc.* **43**, 620.
LEAF, B. and WALL, F. T. (1942). *J. Phys. Chem.* **46**, 820.
LENNARD-JONES, J. E. See FOWLER, R., *Statistical Mechanics*, ch. 10, 1936. Cambridge University Press.
LORENTZ, H. A. (1905). *Proc. Amst. Acad.* **7**, 438, 585, 684.
LUDWIG, C. (1856). *S.B. Akad. Wiss. Wien*, **20**, 539.
LUGG, J. W. H. (1929). *Phil. Mag.* [7] **8**, 1019.

McINTEER, B. B, ALDRICH, L. T. and NIER, A. O. (1947). *Phys. Rev.* **72**, 510.
McINTEER, B. B., ALDRICH, L. T. and NIER, A. O. (1948). *Phys. Rev.* **74**, 946.
MANN, A. K. (1948). *Phys. Rev.* **73**, 412.
MAXWELL, J. C. (1867). *Philos. Trans.* **157**, 49.
MAXWELL, J. C. (1879). *Philos. Trans.* **170**, 231.
MEIXNER, J. (1941). *Ann. Phys., Lpz.*, **39**, 333.
MEIXNER, J. (1942). *Ann. Phys., Lpz.*, **41**, 409.
MEIXNER, J. (1943*a*). *Ann. Phys., Lpz.*, **43**, 244.
MEIXNER, J. (1943*b*). *Z. Phys. Chem.* B, **53**, 235.
MILLER, L. (1949). *Z. Naturforsch.* **4***a*, 262.
MULLIKEN, R. S. (1922). *J. Amer. Chem. Soc.* **44**, 1033.
MURPHEY, B. F. (1947). *Phys. Rev.* **72**, 834.

NIER, A. O. (1939). *Phys. Rev.* **56**, 1009.
NIER, A. O. (1940*a*). *Phys. Rev.* **57**, 30.
NIER, A. O. (1940*b*). *Phys. Rev.* **57**, 338.
NIER, A. O. (1940*c*). *Rev. Sci. Instrum.* **11**, 212.

ONSAGER, L. (1931*a*). *Phys. Rev.* **37**, 405.
ONSAGER, L. (1931*b*). *Phys. Rev.* **38**, 2265.

PRIGOGINE, I. (1947). *Étude thermodynamique des phénomènes irreversibles.* Liège.
PRIGOGINE, I. (1948). *Bull. Acad. Roy. Belg. Cl. Sci.* **34**, 789, 930.
PRIGOGINE, I., DE BROUCKÈRE, L. and AMAND, R. (1950). *Physica*, **16**, 577.
PUSCHNER, M. (1937). *Z. Phys.* **106**, 597.

SCHÄFER, K. and CORTE, H. (1946). *Naturwissenschaften*, **33**, 92.
SCHMAHL, N. G. and SCHEWE, J. (1940). *Z. Elektrochem.* **46**, 203.
SHIBATA, Z. and KITAGAWA, H. (1938). *J. Fac. Sci. Hokkaido Univ.* Sec. III, **2**, 223.
SIMON, R. (1946). *Phys. Rev.* **69**, 596.
SORET, C. (1879). *Arch. Sci. Phys. Nat. Genève* (3), **2**, 48.
SORET, C. (1880*a*). *C.R. Acad. Sci., Paris*, **91**, 289.
SORET, C. (1880*b*). *Arch. Sci. Phys. Nat. Genève* (3), **4**, 209.
SORET, C. (1881). *Ann. Chim. (Phys.)* (5), **22**, 293.
STIER, L. G. (1942). *Phys. Rev.* **62**, 548.

TANNER, C. C. (1927). *Trans. Faraday Soc.* **23**, 75.
DE TROYER, A., VAN ITTERBEEK, A. and VAN DEN BERG, G. J. (1950). *Physica*, **16**, 669.
DE TROYER, A., VAN ITTERBEEK, A. and RIETVELD, A. O. (1951). *Physica*, **17**, 938.

VASILESCO, V. (1945). *Ann. Phys., Paris*, **20**, 292.

WALDMANN, L. (1939). *Z. Phys.* **114**, 53.
WALDMANN, L. (1943). *Z. Phys.* **121**, 501.
WALDMANN, L. (1946). *Z. Naturforsch.* **1**, 59.
WALDMANN, L. (1947*a*). *Z. Phys.* **124**, 2.
WALDMANN, L. (1947*b*). *Z. Phys.* **124**, 175.
WALDMANN, L. (1947*c*). *Z. Naturforsch.* **2***a*, 358.
WALDMANN, L. (1949). *Z. Naturforsch.* **4***a*, 105.
WATSON, W. and WOERNLEY, D. (1943). *Phys. Rev.* **63**, 181.
WEREIDE, T. (1914). *Ann. Phys., Paris*, (9), **2**, 55.
WHALLEY, E. and WINTER, E. R. S. (1949). *Trans. Faraday Soc.* **45**, 1091.
WHALLEY, E., WINTER, E. R. S. and BRISCOE, H. V. A. (1949). *Trans. Faraday Soc.* **45**, 1085.
WINN, E. B. (1950). *Phys. Rev.* **80**, 1024.

YANG, L. M. (1949). *Proc. Roy. Soc.* A, **198**, 471.

LIST OF SYMBOLS

The notation of the first part of this monograph corresponds with that used by Chapman and Cowling in their *Mathematical Theory of Non-Uniform Gases* (1939).

Clarendon type is used for vectors. The figures in brackets indicate the page where the symbol first appears. Subscripts $_{1,2}$ refer to molecules of the first kind (1) or second kind (2), excepting when applied to S and Q.

A ratio of collision integrals of type Ω_{12}. (26)

B ratio of collision integrals of type Ω_{12}. (26)

b a collision parameter; the distance between a molecule A and the direction of motion of another B (relative to A) when beyond the range of interaction. (18)

C ratio of collision integrals of type Ω_{12}. (26)

$\mathbf{C}$ thermal velocity of a molecule; $\mathbf{C} = \mathbf{c} - \bar{\mathbf{c}}$. (5)

$\mathbf{c}$ velocity of a molecule with respect to an arbitrary reference frame (5); $d\mathbf{c}$ an element of volume in velocity space; $d\mathbf{c} = du\,dv\,dw$, where u, v, w are components of $\mathbf{c}$. (16)

$\bar{\mathbf{c}}$ mean molecular velocity (5); for a binary mixture, $n\bar{\mathbf{c}} = n_1 \bar{\mathbf{c}}_1 + n_2 \bar{\mathbf{c}}_2$.

D_{12} coefficient of (concentration) diffusion. (6)

D_T coefficient of thermal diffusion. (6)

$\partial_e f/\partial t$ rate of change of distribution function due to collisions. (18)

$(\partial_e f_1/\partial t)_2$ rate of change of distribution function for molecules 1 due to collisions with molecules 2. (20)

$(\partial/\partial \mathbf{r}).\boldsymbol{\phi}$ divergence of $\boldsymbol{\phi}$, $\left(\dfrac{\partial \phi_x}{\partial x} + \dfrac{\partial \phi_y}{\partial y} + \dfrac{\partial \phi_z}{\partial z}\right)$. (80)

$\partial \psi/\partial \mathbf{r}$ gradient of ψ; components $\partial \psi/\partial x$, $\partial \psi/\partial y$, $\partial \psi/\partial z$. (6)

E_1 a function of collision integrals of types Ω_1, Ω_{12} ($E_1 = M_1 E/[\mu_1]_1$ of *M.T.*). (26)

E_2 a function of collision integrals of types Ω_2, Ω_{12} ($E_2 = M_2 E/[\mu_2]_1$ of *M.T.*). (26)

$f(\mathbf{c}, \mathbf{r}, t)$ distribution function such that $f\,d\mathbf{c}\,d\mathbf{r}$ is the number of molecules with velocities in element $d\mathbf{c}$ and positions in element $d\mathbf{r}$. (16)

g   relative velocity of two molecules. (18)

k Boltzmann constant. (17)

k_T thermal diffusion ratio, D_T/D_{12}. (6)

M the proportionate mass difference, $M_1 - M_2$. (26)

M_1 mass ratio, m_1/m_0. (24)

M_2 mass ratio, m_2/m_0. (24)

m mass of a molecule. (14)

m_0 $m_1 + m_2$. (24)

N_0 Avogadro's number. (63)

n number density of molecules. (6)

n_{10} proportion of molecules 1; $n_{10} = n_1/(n_1 + n_2)$. (6)

n_{20} proportion of molecules 2; $n_{20} = n_2/(n_1 + n_2)$. (6)

p pressure of gas. (63)

Q_1, Q_2, Q_{12} quantities in the expression for k_T and α. (26)

q the separation factor. (37)

q   heat flux density. (23)

r   radius vector; $d\mathbf{r}$, an element of volume $= dx\,dy\,dz$. (17)

R gas constant per mole. (63)

R_T the thermal separation ratio; $R_T = \dfrac{\alpha}{[\alpha(\infty)]_1}$. (33)

S the thermal separation; the difference in composition in the two parts of the diffusion vessel in the equilibrium state. (36)

S_1, S_2 quantities in the expression for k_T. (26)

s the change in composition in one part of the diffusion vessel. (37)

T temperature; in particular the temperature of the colder part of the diffusion vessel. (6)

T' the temperature of the hotter part of the diffusion vessel. (7)

W collision integrals. (69)

α the thermal diffusion factor; $\alpha = \dfrac{k_T}{n_{10}n_{20}}$. (7)

$\alpha(\infty)$ for rigid elastic spheres. (34)

Γ molecular flux density. (13)

ϵ minimum potential energy of interaction of two molecules, taken as positive. (31)

κ force constant. (25)

λ coefficient of thermal conductivity. (23)

μ coefficient of viscosity. (24)

ν force index. (25)

ρ density of a gas. (81)

σ diameter of a molecule. (25)

Σ_1 ratio of molecular diameters; $\Sigma_1 = \dfrac{\sigma_1}{\sigma_1 + \sigma_2}$. (29)

Σ_2 ratio of molecular diameters; $\Sigma_2 = \dfrac{\sigma_2}{\sigma_1 + \sigma_2}$. (29)

Σ proportionate diameter difference; $\Sigma = \Sigma_1 - \Sigma_2$. (29)

τ relaxation time. (125)

$\phi^{(l)}$ an integral which enters into the collision integrals. (24)

χ the angular deflexion of one molecule in an encounter with another. (18)

$\Omega^{(l)}(r)$ collision integrals. (24)

ν force index. (34)

ρ density of a gas. (31)

σ diameter of a molecule. (25)

Σ_{12} ratio of molecular diameters; $\Sigma_{12} = \dfrac{\sigma_1}{\sigma_{12}}$ (29)

Σ ratio of molecular diameters; $\Sigma = \dfrac{\sigma_1}{\sigma_2}$ (30)

Σ proportionate diameter difference; $\Sigma = \sigma_1 - \sigma_2$ (29)

τ relaxation time. (135)

φ an integral which enters into the collision integrals. (34)

χ the angular deflection of one molecule in an encounter with another. (18)

$\Omega^{(l)}(r)$ collision integrals. (24)

INDEX